LYDIA LONGLEY, *The First American Nun*

Lydia Longley

THE FIRST AMERICAN NUN

by Helen A. McCarthy

illustrated by John Lawn

VISION BOOKS

Farrar, Straus & Cudahy   New York
Burns & Oates   London

VISION BOOKS IS A DIVISION OF
FARRAR, STRAUS & CUDAHY, INC.
PUBLISHED SIMULTANEOUSLY IN CANADA BY
AMBASSADOR BOOKS, LTD., TORONTO.
MANUFACTURED IN THE UNITED STATES OF AMERICA.

L
92
m

Dec., 1967

Dedicated to
Dan and Sheila
Who gave me courage and inspiration
when it was needed most

Nihil Obstat:
Rt. Rev. Msgr. Peter B. O'Connor
Censor Librorum

Imprimatur:
✠ Most Reverend Thomas A. Boland, S.T.D.
Archbishop of Newark

CONTENTS

Author's Note

I discovered Lydia Longley quite by chance while reading a brief account of her family in Dr. Samuel Green's *History of Groton*. I was interested in the misleading statement that she was "*placed* in the Congregation de Notre Dame." The present mother superior of the Congregation de Notre Dame in Montreal helped me discover the true dramatic story I knew must be hidden in the records of the past.

I found not only a stirring story, but an important historical link, for Lydia Longley was the first religious to have been born in what is now the United States. The result of my research is this book, the first biography of Lydia Longley.

All of the major incidents and characters are true, but, in a few cases, fictitious names have been supplied for minor characters whose names history has forgotten. Based on what is known of life in both Groton and Ville-Marie during that period, Lydia's story has been drawn from material in some twenty volumes. These include accounts of Puritan life in early New England, histories of Groton and Shirley, Massachusetts, histories of Canada and Montreal, and biographies of Jeanne LeBer and Mother Marguerite Bourgeoys, foundress of the Congregation de Notre Dame.

I.

The Longleys of Groton

Lydia Longley always remembered the day her father announced he was bringing home a brand-new mother to take care of his children.

"I have something to tell you," he said one summer morning at breakfast. "I hope it will make you as happy as it has made me. Ever since your mother died, we've been lonely. We've all missed her love and understanding. Many a time I've seen loneliness on your faces—especially on yours, Lydia."

He smiled at his eldest child. "A man needs a woman to give him companionship, and you children need a mother. You've been my right hand, Lydia, but it's too much to expect a girl of eleven to be a mother to three little ones."

Lydia looked at her brother Will, a year younger than she, but tall for his age; at Jemima, aged five, and at little John, just three. Yes, it was true. It had been no easy task to care for all of them. But a new mother . . . ! Lydia frowned a bit.

"This afternoon, my dears," her father went on, "the Widow Crisp and I are to be married at the magistrate's house. Deliverance has consented to become your new mother, and I hope you will love her dearly."

As Will and Jemima clapped and squealed with delight, little John clapped too, though he didn't know why. Only Lydia was silent. She had seen the widow at the meetinghouse where the good Puritans of Groton, Massachusetts, gathered on the Sabbath. She wished now that she had noticed Mrs. Crisp more closely. I wonder if she will love us and be as good to us as Mother was, Lydia thought. What will it be like to have a stranger telling us what to do, living here in Mother's place?

The other children were so busy asking questions and making plans that Lydia's silence was unnoticed. Her father left to do his morning chores and the youngsters started their housework.

"Won't it be wonderful to have a new mother, Lydia?" asked Jemima later as they cleared the table board and stacked the dishes.

"I suppose it will be." Lydia spoke slowly and a little uncertainly. "Now we must clean the house so that it will be spotless. She'll probably be looking all around. I do hope she likes us!"

"I'm going to gather some violets for her," Jemima continued, as if she had not heard her sister. "I know where there are some at the edge of the woods."

"I think I'll give her my robin's egg," offered Will as he filled the wood box. "It's so blue—a real beauty."

Even little John piped up with a babyish, "Want to give her a present, too!" They all laughed and promised that his new mother would like *his* gift best of all.

Time passed quickly as the Longleys flew about sweeping floors and polishing pewter. Lydia's thoughts were in a turmoil.

I know I should give her something, she worried. The only thing I have is my sampler, and she might not like it. My stitches aren't even—and I don't know that I want her to have it, anyway. I'll *never* forget our own mother!

After dinner, Mr. Longley kissed them good-by. Dressed in his best clothes, he looked very solemn and dignified as he drove off in the wagon. The excited youngsters crowded onto the steps of the log house to watch him.

"We'll change into our best clothes, too," announced Lydia suddenly, "and have tea all ready when they get here."

"Let's!" Jemima and Will shouted gleefully.

"Let's!" echoed John.

A little later they were again on the steps watching the narrow dirt road.

"They're coming," shouted Will. A cloud of dust appeared in the distance.

Lydia's heart was pounding as the old wagon came into sight. Two faces turned toward the children, and the woman waved. Then they were out of the wagon and she was smiling at them.

"This is your new mother," William Longley said simply. Deliverance's face was shining as she stooped over to put her arms around Lydia first. Kissing her, she said, "How wonderful to have such a beautiful ready-made daughter!"

Lydia looked up at her father and was surprised to see tears in his eyes. Then Deliverance hugged the other children one by one, laughing and crying at the same time. Impulsively Lydia ran into the house, lifted the cover of the settle by the hearth, and took out her sampler. She turned around just as they came into the kitchen.

Deliverance was exclaiming with delight as she buried her face in the fragrant bouquet Jemima had thrust into her hand. Lydia watched her take, with a surprised smile, Will's blue robin's egg. Then Deliverance hugged John as he held out a bruised little buttercup. Lydia summoned up her courage and stepped forward.

"I'd like you to have this," she said, shyly extending her sampler. "I finished it just yesterday," she added apologetically, "and it isn't very good."

Deliverance gently took the framed cloth on which letters and numbers were cross-stitched in colored thread. "Thank you, dear. It's beautiful." She smiled as she turned to her husband. "You are all so sweet. God has been good to me this day."

God continued to be good to the Longleys. Four more children were born and, despite the ruggedness of life in colonial New England and the constant threat of attack by Indians, they were a happy family.

As Lydia and Jemima walked side by side toward the meetinghouse one Sabbath morning, that threat of attack seemed to be closer to Groton than ever. Nine years had passed since Deliverance had come to them. Lydia had become a tall, slender twenty-year-old with curly brown hair.

The elder Longleys led the family procession to church while Will walked in the rear. Both Mr. Longley and Will carried guns.

Deliverance and the girls wore dark dresses with white lawn collars and caps. The boys looked unnaturally neat and dignified in knee breeches, doublets and broad white collars. Lydia, Jemima and John took turns carrying the baby.

At the end of their road Lydia glanced up at the garrison house. The high fence surrounding it had openings where guns could be placed. The great gate through the high timber wall was open, and Lydia unconsciously slowed her steps.

"What are you looking at, Lydia?" Jemima whispered, for they were not supposed to chat on the way to meeting. Deliverance always said they must have respect for the Lord's Day and walk with dignity.

"I'm thinking about the time four years ago when we all came here because the soldier warned Father of an attack," she said softly. "It turned out to be a false alarm, though. You remember, don't you?"

Jemima nodded. "I remember how scared I was. But John said he hoped there *would* be an attack, that it would be exciting."

"He didn't know what he was saying. We've been lucky so far."

"Are you afraid we'll be attacked by Indians, Lydia?" Jemima asked breathlessly.

"I don't know. Sometimes when I'm in the garden, or down at the brook, I feel as if someone were watching me. It's probably my imagination."

Their father looked around with raised eyebrows and motioned for quiet. Jemima lowered her eyes and the girls walked on in silence.

The meetinghouse was about a mile from the Longley farm. At the door the family separated and took the seats which had been assigned to them. There were rough benches on the main floor of the large, bare room and also in the gallery which ran around three sides. Single men and women sat apart, as did boys and girls, but husbands and wives remained together. Deacons occupied the front pew. When Pastor Hobart and his family entered, everyone stood up until he reached the pulpit.

Today Lydia's thoughts wandered. She noticed that several boys were rapped on the knuckles for whispering or giggling. The pastor's prayer lasted at least an hour and the sermon was even longer.

Then came the psalm-singing. One of the deacons set the key and sang a line, slowly intoning each word from the psalm book. Then the congregation sang it together, repeating the words after him. Lydia's sweet voice rang out so clearly that Jemima nudged her and grinned.

After the service, as the Longleys were about to start for home, Captain Parker of the militia hurried up and drew Mr. Longley aside.

Lydia could hear the captain's low voice. "There's Indian trouble north of us, William. Some of the militiamen who got back yesterday tell of bloodshed."

Mr. Longley's face was grave as he glanced back at his family. "We must be constantly on our guard,

Captain," he whispered fiercely. "The destruction of eighteen years ago must not be repeated."

Lydia was still thinking about that conversation the next morning as she worked around the big kitchen.

She set the last wooden bowl of corn-meal mush on the long table and went to the doorway. The hot July sun was rising in the east beyond the clearing, but the early morning breeze was cool on her cheeks.

"Breakfast's ready," she called loudly. "Come on, everybody."

Deliverance was pouring milk into wooden mugs as Jemima helped three-year-old Betty dress in one corner of the cluttered room. Lydia knew that soon the baby would awaken in the north chamber and whimper for attention.

Mr. Longley strode into the kitchen and stood at the head of the table until the boys rushed into their places. They had been doing early morning chores about the farm and had stopped to splash themselves in the basin on a bench just outside the kitchen door. Mr. Longley paused a moment as Jemima and Betty darted across the room. Then, bowing his head, he began the prayer of thanksgiving.

Lydia's blue eyes centered on her family as they hungrily consumed the mush and milk. There was Will, nineteen years old, big and dependable and handsome, her father's right-hand man. Jemima, fourteen, already a fine little housewife, could sew, knit, and cook as well as their mother. John, twelve, loved to hunt and fish and hated the lessons which Lydia, as the oldest, gave to the younger children. Joseph, eight, adored John and followed him from morning till night like an obedient slave. Richard, six, mischievous and fun-loving, was always getting hurt. Betty, little and frail, was the pet of the household, in danger of being spoiled until the coming of Baby Nathaniel eight months before.

As Lydia helped her stepmother refill porridge bowls, the sound of little Nathaniel's crying interrupted her thoughts. She hurried to drag his cradle out into the kitchen.

"He likes to be with us," she said to Deliverance, who had dropped down onto a stool to eat a hasty bite. Following the family rule, the children were eating quickly and in silence. Only Will and Lydia were allowed to talk with their father and mother, for Puritan children were "seen but not heard" at mealtime.

"We'll start haying, Will, right after breakfast," Mr. Longley said. "It's going to be a good day and maybe we can finish up out there. Joseph, you and Richard pick a mess of huckleberries for your mother. John, you must get the day's supply of wash water down at the brook. We'll all be hungry this noon, Deliverance," he added with a twinkle, as he helped himself to a piece of corn-meal bread. Deliverance smiled understandingly.

It was July, 1694, almost forty years since the first pioneers had arrived in the frontier town of Groton. Lydia's Grandfather Longley had come from England as one of those first settlers. Her father had often told her of Grandfather—the tall, straight, gruff town clerk whom she could barely remember, for she had been only six when he died.

Father sometimes told about the terrible Indian raid on Groton when Lydia was only two years old—the one he and Captain Parker had referred to outside the meetinghouse. The family had fled to Lynn. When they returned to Groton, they had found it deserted and burned to the ground, so Grandfather and Father had built by themselves the rough-hewn log house. Now Grandfather was dead and Father was William Longley, Senior, the honored and respected town clerk.

As Lydia ate her mush in silence, Deliverance picked up the baby. The boys, all except John, had left with their father. The two younger ones took pails for the huckleberries which grew nearby. John walked slowly down the hill toward the brook, a yoke slung across his shoulders and empty pails swinging. With the yoke he could carry two pails full of water at a time.

Betty stood at the open door crooning to the wooden doll Grandmother Longley had brought over from England when Lydia was a little girl. Lydia and Deliverance had taught Jemima to sew by making doll clothes. How they had all loved that poppet! As Lydia watched Betty pat the chipped, faded face, she recalled the days she herself had spent playing with the big wooden "baby." How badly she had missed it on Sabbath days when Puritan children were not allowed to play!

Lydia jumped up to help Jemima clear the table board and lift it over to a corner of the room until the next meal. She swept the worn floor with the broom of birch twigs which Will and John had made in the spring. Then, as she bent over the fireplace to stir the kettle of Indian pudding simmering there, she thought again uneasily of the Indian danger.

"Mother, do you think the Indians might attack?" she asked her stepmother suddenly. "I overheard what Captain Parker told Father yesterday and I've never seen him so concerned."

"There's always that danger in a frontier settlement, Lydia," answered Deliverance seriously. "With England and France at war in Europe, hostilities are continued over here in the colonies. The French, you know, are Papists and hate Puritans. Some say they spur on the Indians to attack our settlements. From time to time we hear that both Indians and French come down from New France, north of us, to invade our villages."

Lydia straightened to face Deliverance. "But if Groton folks are worried about an Indian attack, why don't they leave here as they did in 1676?"

"They can't do that now without a special license, and that's too expensive for most of us to buy. Without a license we'd lose all rights to our land," Deliverance explained, lifting little Nathaniel to her shoulder and patting him gently.

"Whoever decided that?" asked Jemima. She

had taken hot water from the kettle on the hearth, poured it into the dishpan on the bench outside, and had started to wash the breakfast bowls, mugs, and wooden spoons.

"The General Court," answered Deliverance, "and I think your father *is* worried for fear there'll be a sudden attack on the village. He told me yesterday that the boys shouldn't go hunting or fishing alone in the woods. I know he was thinking of John especially, for he slips away sometimes and doesn't let us know where he is going."

"Who's talking about me?" asked John, appearing suddenly from around the corner of the house. He had emptied the two pails of water into the rinse tub and was about to start down the hill for another load. "We need some meat, Mother. May I go hunting when I finish getting the water? Anyway, I want to look at my traps. There may be some rabbits in them."

"I would like to make some rabbit stew," said Deliverance. "Perhaps your father will let you go to your traps with Lydia after dinner. They're not too far into the forest."

John turned away and Deliverance spoke again. "We've got lots to do this morning, girls. Jemima, go out into the garden and get some beans, will you? Look and see how Richard and Joseph are getting along picking berries. Like as not, Richard is up in a tree! And take Betty with you. She'll help you pick beans in her baby fashion." Deliverance smiled at the child on the step.

"Lydia, will you do the washing while I get at the cottage cheese? Make up the beds first, though. I guess we'll have venison for dinner. I wish John could get a wild turkey. My mouth is watering for some turkey, and I've seen a lot of them flying around here lately."

She walked over to the window. "Your father hasn't time to go hunting with all this haying ahead of him," she said thoughtfully.

"He's got lots of help this morning," added Lydia, as she, too, looked out across the fields. "I suppose Will and Father will have to do their share helping the others when their hay is ready."

Lydia went into her parents' bedroom first and made up the big feather bed. As she spread back the patchwork coverlet, she thought of how she had enjoyed helping Deliverance make it. They had arranged little squares of cloth in the form of a large colorful star, featherstitching each tiny piece sep-

arately with painstaking perseverance. Lydia loved
to sew.

Then she hurried into the small back chamber to
smooth up Betty's trundle bed and her own and
Jemima's flock bed with its mattress stuffed with
rags, feathers, and wool shearings.

"When will Father go over to Unquety Meadows to see if our cows are all right?" Lydia asked
Deliverance before climbing the steep ladder stairs
to the garret where the four boys slept. On very
warm nights they brought their straw ticks downstairs into the airy kitchen, for the garret was close
and uncomfortable.

On the far side of the loft hung bunches of dried
herbs and roots—saffron, sage, dandelion, catnip,
and mint. Lydia sniffed their fragrance. Deliverance
had learned how to use these to good advantage
when the children were ill.

"I don't know when he'll get over to the meadows. He may have to send Will over tomorrow
with one of the older boys from the neighborhood.
Your father hasn't gone to Unquety for two or three
weeks. Soon they'll be haying at Rock Meadow,
too. I always dread to have them go over there; it's
Indian country."

"I know," said Lydia, as she hung some of the boys' clothing on pegs. Every year at haying time Deliverance spoke fearfully of Rock Meadow.

Like most of his farmer neighbors, William Longley did not have enough meadow land near his house to provide hay for his cattle in winter. He owned small scattered pieces of lowland, like Unquety Meadows, in Groton and even as far away as Lancaster. It was the custom in Groton and other villages to grant small pieces of meadow land to farmers who didn't have enough around their homes. Rock Meadow was one of these pieces which was divided among Longley and his neighbors. In this way Lydia's father was able to produce enough hay to feed his livestock. That was the important thing with a family of eight children.

Lydia went outside with an armful of clothing. She filled the tub with hot water from the big kettle always kept on the hearth and then added cold water from the rain barrel. John had filled the rinse tub by this time, and he helped her. Pouring home-made soap into the tub, she began to use the scrubbing stick.

After washing and rinsing the clothing, she hung

pieces of it on the surrounding bushes to dry and on the grass to whiten in the sun.

"You haven't finished getting enough water for the whole day, John," Lydia called to her brother in the barnyard. "The men will be coming over to get cooled off, and they'll want to wash up."

"I'll be right back," said John. "I want to see Snowball." He ran over to the pet lamb standing in the group of three or four sheep. How he loves that lamb, thought Lydia, as John caressed it and the lamb nuzzled him in return.

It was almost dinnertime when Lydia finished cleaning up the tubs and stood looking about the farm. A fragrant odor of broiling meat came from the kitchen.

Beyond the cornfield the men were pitching hay into carts and packing the loads. Suddenly there were screams and shouts from the direction of the huckleberry patch. Joseph and Richard raced toward Lydia.

2.

JOHN'S TURKEY

"At least they aren't hurt," Lydia said to Deliverance who had appeared in the doorway. "I can see both boys now." Jemima and Betty ran to the edge of the vegetable garden to meet their brothers.

"A snake! A snake! We saw a huge black snake this big!" screamed Richard, stretching out his arms.

"I almost stepped on it," shouted Joseph.

"Where are your berries?" asked their mother,

disappointedly. "I was planning on them for dinner. Snakes around here won't hurt you."

"We left them over there." The youngsters pointed.

"I don't want to go back now," sobbed Richard, tears running down his berry-stained cheeks. "I'm afraid!"

"They're more afraid of you than you are of them," scoffed Lydia, although she was a little afraid of snakes herself.

John, who had finished drawing the water, said with a scornful look at Richard, "Oh, I'll get those old berries."

"I guess I'll go with John," decided Joseph, as Richard went into the house with Deliverance. Lydia watched the boys striding across the clearing. John is almost as tall as Will, she thought. And he's a wonderful helper. He'll make a fine farmer.

"I'm afraid to go back into the garden," Betty said to her. "Guess I'll stay here. I feel so safe with you," she added, and Lydia stooped to give the little girl a hug. Jemima went back to the vegetable garden to finish filling her pail with beans.

"Snakes *are* horrid things," Lydia admitted to her little sister. "Let's go in and help mother get dinner.

She's making cottage cheese and must be nearly finished by now."

The Longley house was more comfortable than many in 1694. About a mile and a half from the center of Groton, it was the last dwelling on the narrow dirt road and was bounded on one side by thick forest. On the other stretched acres of rolling fields. The nearest neighbor lived a quarter of a mile away. In winter, when the trees were bare, the Longleys could see smoke rising from their neighbor's chimney.

William Longley and his father had built their house of hewn logs laid horizontally and chinked with clay. There was a small front entrance. The windows were sliding panels of board, and the inside walls were clapboards grooved together and molded at the joints.

The three downstairs rooms included a large kitchen, the north chamber, and a small back bedroom or lean-to. From the kitchen crude and steep ladder-like stairs led up into the loft which extended across only the front part of the house. The chimney was of fieldstone, though many of the houses about the outskirts of the village still had wooden ones which often caught fire.

The fireplace extended almost across one side of the kitchen, which was used as the family living room. There was no mantelpiece, but a heavy wooden beam called the manteltree stretched across the top of the fireplace. A lug pole hung over the burning logs upon which were suspended pots and pans and a supply of hot water in an iron kettle.

A hazelwood spit, whittled by hand, was thrust through some deer meat which sizzled and gave off a fragrant aroma. High-backed benches called settles stood at either side of the hearth to keep drafts from chilling those seated there in cold weather. Their boxed seats stored bedding and clothing. The children sat on stools or blocks of wood in front of the fire and enjoyed toasting chestnuts on fall evenings.

Shelves along the wall held wooden and pewter utensils for eating and cooking. A dye tub had its place in the overcrowded room, along with the loom, spinning wheel, and flax wheel. The oak table board rested against the wall between meals. Several chests held skeins of wool and homespun clothing which Deliverance and Lydia had made. On the wall hung a cheese closet, a set of shelves covered with cheesecloth which held cheeses Deliverance made in the summertime.

In Lydia's chamber stood her oaken dower chest, well filled with linens and homespuns. She worried, though, because she had not yet fallen in love. Even though contacts between Puritan young men and women were few, most girls were married at twenty. One or two of the village boys had spoken to her father about Lydia, but they did not seem to interest her.

In Lydia's parents' room the bed was complete with curtains and valances, the only one in the house canopied. Lydia was glad her bed was open. She loved the fresh, cold air. She enjoyed looking out over the clearing behind the house, seeing the twinkling stars and occasionally a flashing meteor, listening to the whippoorwills and the hoot of an owl in the woods.

The Longley cellar was William's pride. Here were stored the family provisions—meats, root crops, butter, preserves, milk, eggs, and cider. This cellar could withstand all kinds of disaster, William would boast to his family, for it was well constructed.

During late winter afternoons the spinning wheel whirred with a merry hum as Deliverance, in her homespun gown, busily worked at her wheel. Richard and Joseph would fill the quills for the next day's work as their mother took skeins of wool from the chest at her side. When Grandmother Longley lived with them, she had done most of the spinning.

Candles made by Deliverance and Lydia were used for artificial light. Pine torches, really short sections of dry pine logs from the heart of the wood, were cut into eight-or ten-inch strips and placed in holders which stood at the fireplace. The resinous quality of the wood caused the splinters to burn like torches. Flat stones caught their drippings. The children loved to see the kitchen after nightfall when several torches burned at one time and roaring logs cast a bright glow about the room. The intense heat cast by the fire made it impractical in warm weather, though, so during the summer months the family was usually in bed by dark.

A shed connected the kitchen with the barn so that the boys could feed the animals without going outside. Horses, sheep, and cattle were kept in the barn, and there were several outhouses which pro-

vided shelter for chickens and a storage place for
firewood and farm implements.

According to farm custom, neighbors who
helped William with his haying were invited to
share the noon meal with the family. Despite the
extra work, the girls and Deliverance enjoyed having the neighbors in for dinner. It was not often that
they had guests, and, as they hurried about refilling
empty trenchers, they listened with keen relish to
the bits of gossip and news discussed by the men and
boys. They ate later with the children.

Today the table board was scrubbed so clean it
was almost white. Trenchers were heaped with
broiled venison, Indian pudding, carrots, peas, and
Indian bannock. The ill-fated huckleberries were
saved for the children's dessert, and the men ate pies
which had been stored in the cool cellar. Besides
milk, there was cider to quench the thirst.

Lydia and Jemima, in their homespun dresses
and calico aprons, hurried back and forth waiting
on the workers. John, who was eating with the men,
leaned over to his father.

"Excuse me, sir," he said respectfully. "May I
go to the woods and check my traps this afternoon?

Mother says our fresh meat is getting low and she hopes I might find some rabbits in them."

"I don't want you in the woods alone, John," his father replied, frowning. "We need meat, though, and neither Will nor I can leave the haying, so I'll let you and Lydia go—but only as far as the snares—and providing your mother consents! Both of you are good shots."

He turned to the others at the table. "Perhaps I'm overcareful. We haven't had Indian trouble for many years, but still I don't like what I hear from the north, nor from some of the other English colonies."

Lydia glanced at Deliverance, who nodded her permission.

"I'll go with John, Father," she said. At the same time she knew, though she would never admit, that she was frightened. There was an uneasy, upset feeling in the pit of her stomach. There's no danger so close to home, she told herself, and we both have rifles. Still she could not quiet her fears.

John's face was wreathed in smiles. He'd rather hunt and trap in the woods than eat, Lydia reflected.

"You'd better take my rifle, Lydia," said Will. "There's something wrong with yours. I tried it yesterday and I mean to fix it for you when I have the time."

"Thank you, Will," answered Lydia gratefully, pouring more milk into his empty mug. "I wish you were coming with us."

Jemima flashed a quick glance in Lydia's direction. She knows I'm afraid to go into the forest even a little way, thought the older girl. I mustn't be such a coward.

Deliverance was busy at the fireplace preparing more meat for the children's dinner. As the men filed out of the room, Jemima and Lydia cleared the trenchers and other utensils. Quickly washing them, the two girls soon had the table board ready for the second meal.

"Hurry up and eat, Lydia," said John impatiently, as he took down the rifles, powder horn, and shot from their places on the wall. He started to load the guns while Lydia ate her dinner.

"I must help mother and Jemima clean up the kitchen," said his sister, "but I'll start as soon as I can. You've got plenty to do, too, before we go," she added sternly, at the same time noticing how tired Deliverance looked. "If we didn't need the meat so badly, I should stay at home and let you rest, Mother."

Many Puritan girls were not allowed to shoot, for it was considered unladylike. The task of providing fish and game for the family fell to the men and boys. Mr. Longley was one who believed that Lydia should learn how to handle a rifle for her own protection, and she could shoot as well as her brother, Will, with whom she usually went hunting. At twelve, John was the natural huntsman of the family, in spite of the fact that he had had his own rifle just a year. Unusually tall and muscular for his age, he was often mistaken for a fourteen- or fifteen-year-old.

An hour later the tall, slender girl followed her strapping brother, Indian fashion in a single file, down a narrow path near the house toward the woods. The boys and their father had cleared away the underbrush so that this spot was a kind of grove, delightfully cool and shady. Now and then a chipmunk or squirrel darted across their path. John stopped a moment, taking a deep breath.

He turned to Lydia. "I love to get away from the house. The traps are down near Cold Spring. I can hardly wait to see what luck I've had!"

Lydia smiled at the boy's eagerness as she watched him slip quietly through the woods. He made almost no sound on the soft bed of pine needles. Lydia had hard work to keep up with him.

As they advanced more deeply into the underbrush, Lydia was glad that she had thought to wear Will's boots, for the walking was more difficult here. Cold Spring was about a quarter of a mile from home, and many rabbits, deer, and other wild animals frequented the area. Suddenly, John stopped and bent over to investigate some tracks around a hole in a tree trunk.

"That might be a foxhole. I ought to make a trap and catch him some day soon," he said, as if to himself.

Lydia hadn't been hunting with John for some time. "What kind of traps have you built at Cold Spring?" she asked.

"They're snares, really," John replied, pleased because Lydia had asked about them. "Will showed me how to make a snare which would snap up when the rabbit was caught. I bend a sapling down over the path of the rabbit run. When the rabbit gets caught in the snare, the sapling snaps up, taking him with it. Then, you see, he is held up high out of reach of the other forest animals."

Lydia stooped down to pick some checkerberry leaves and nibble on them. Their pungent flavor stung her tongue a bit. She sniffed the small leaves appreciatively as they walked on.

"Look at the beautiful green moss and the ferns, John," she pointed out as her brother made a flying leap across a brook. She followed him as well as she could, hampered by her long skirts.

"Quiet, Lydia," John whispered. She heard the sound of "gobble, gobble" coming from above. She followed the aim of his rifle as he lifted it and pointed it toward the branch of a high oak. As he snapped the lock, Lydia heard a crack. The gun went off. There was a flash and a bang and, sure enough, something plummeted through the branches. John shouted with delight.

"I got him!" he exclaimed as he ran over to the spot where the beautiful bird had fallen.

"A wild turkey!" Lydia said, admiring the brilliant feathers of blue, green, and violet.

"A big one!" laughed John. "It must weigh close to twenty pounds."

"What luck! Won't Mother be pleased?"

Lydia sank down on a fallen log and waited for John to reload his rifle. He could hardly contain himself as he gathered up the bird.

They hurried on to Cold Spring where the snares were comparatively close together, and John was pleased to find two fat rabbits suspended in mid-air. He quickly released them and said importantly to Lydia:

"I guess you'll have to carry the rifles. I'll take the rabbits and turkey. They'll be quite a load."

"Let's rest a minute first and have a drink of water," said Lydia.

They bent over the spring and scooped handfuls of the ice-cold liquid to their flushed faces.

"I wish I were an Indian," said John wistfully as he began to reset the snares.

"John, you can't mean that! Have you forgotten they are our enemies?" asked Lydia, looking uneasily behind her. For all one knew, an Indian brave might be lurking behind every tree trunk. Lydia grasped her rifle more tightly.

"I do mean it," answered the boy. "They're so free. They don't have to go to church or do this and do that around the house. They don't have to dress up or have lessons the way I do."

"Have lessons!" exclaimed Lydia. "Your lessons don't amount to much, you know. I wish we had a school in Groton so we could all learn more. All you can do is read and write a little and do a few simple sums. John Longley, isn't there *anything* you like about being a Puritan boy?"

"I suppose so. I love Mother and Father and all of you—and Snowball," John said falteringly. "And I enjoy Thanksgiving Day and watching the militia men train."

"Don't ever let Father hear you say you'd like to be an Indian! Have you ever stopped to think how brave he was to come out here to Groton and run the risk of being killed by Indians? He could live much more safely and comfortably in Lynn or Charlestown."

"I never thought of that," said John. "Why did he do it?"

"He wanted to have a part in colonizing the wilderness, I expect," answered Lydia. "Perhaps he felt it was his duty, and perhaps the excitement and uncertainty of the life here appealed to him. Surely he works hard clearing the land, plowing, planting, and raising food enough to feed our big family. Just building the house and barn and fences was quite a chore. And Father takes an active part in town affairs, holding office and recording important events which take place here."

"I still think that roaming around the forest all day hunting and fishing and trapping and living in wigwams would be more fun. Indians are strong and healthy, too."

"And cruel," added Lydia. "We'd better be getting along," she said impatiently, for she knew that John would be content to loiter in the woods all the afternoon, imagining himself an Indian lad. "Let's hurry home and show the folks your game. You can feel justly proud of yourself today, John."

As the two neared the house, John broke into a run and shouted, "Mother, look! I've killed a turkey! Look what I've got!"

Carrying the baby in her arms, Deliverance appeared. Jemima and her two little brothers pushed their way past her and tore across the yard at great speed, screaming excitedly, "John's got a turkey! John's got a turkey!"

Lydia watched John's face flush with pride. She smiled at Deliverance as she listened to his detailed description of how he shot the bird.

"It's a big one!" exclaimed Joseph admiringly.

"I'm proud of you, John," praised Deliverance as she led the way into the house. "And your father will be, too," she added. "Mmm—won't it taste good!"

After the four o'clock supper of oatmeal and milk and huckleberry tarts, the kitchen floor was swept clean of crumbs. At five, Deliverance was preparing Nathaniel for bed and would soon be nursing and rocking him to sleep. Lydia's father, with Will and John, was out in the barn doing the milking and the evening chores.

Jemima sat on the stoop diligently working on a colorful sampler. She had nearly completed the end of the verse: "In prosperity friends will be plenty, but in adversity not one in twenty." Her stitches were exquisitely fine. Jemima did beautiful handi-work. Betty was watching Joseph and Richard wrestling in the grass.

Lydia sighed. "Lesson time, boys," she called from the door. "Come, Richard and Joseph, and let me hear you read your letters." The boys half-heartedly started for the house.

"Wash your hands while I get the hornbook and primer and my knitting needle for a pointer," instructed Lydia, going to the shelf which held the

Longley reading material. Here were a Bible, Psalter, hornbook, and New England Primer. She set them on the table board and waited for the youngsters to come in.

Soon Lydia was seated on one of the settles, the two little boys in front of her on stools.

"You may begin, Joseph," she said. "First try saying the alphabet through once from memory."

"Good," she praised as he completed the ABC's in perfect order. Standing up, she hung the hornbook around his neck and pointed first to one letter and then to another, calling upon him to name them.

Their hornbook was old and shabby, for it had seen much usage in the Longley home. Brought over from England many years before by Grandfather Longley, it had been used to teach Lydia, Will, Jemima, and John to read and shape their letters.

Truly it was not a book, but a thin piece of wood, about four or five inches long and two inches wide with a handle attached to its back. The handle was pierced with a hole through which a piece of string ran so that the hornbook could be hung about the neck.

At the two upper corners were crosses. Attached

to the board was a paper on which the alphabet was
printed in capital and small letters. Beneath the alphabet were syllables—ab, eb, ib, ob, and so on. The
Lord's Prayer came below the syllables. The printed
page was covered with a thin sheet of yellowish
horn, somewhat transparent. The children could see
the letters through it and yet the paper was pro-
tected. The paper and horn were fastened to the
edge of the wood by a narrow strip of metal which
was tacked down by fine nails.

As Lydia pointed to the syllables, Joseph sounded
them out in a high little voice. "Ib . . . eb . . .
ab . . . ob," he droned.

"Now, Richard," announced Lydia, putting
the hornbook around his neck, "it's your turn. Close
your eyes, though, and say the alphabet first."

He, too, recited the ABC's promptly and accu-
rately.

"Now your letters," Lydia said patiently, pointing to the letters with her knitting needle.

For ten or fifteen minutes the drill proceeded
with quiet success. Lydia was gratified to see how
well both boys were doing.

"We'll now recite the Lord's Prayer and then
open the primer."

She heard a kick under the table and both lads giggled. She glared at Richard who was usually the principal offender during the lesson hour.

"Joseph," she said promptly, "you may read in the primer first. Start with the rhymes, please."

"In Adam's fall
We sinned all," he read in a singsong manner.

Through the alphabet the youngsters read, first one and then the other, until the last verse was reached.

"Zaccheus he
Did climb a tree
His Lord to see."

Both boys enjoyed reading from the primer and giggled when the verses tickled their funny bones. The pictures, although small and faded now, were still exciting. The burning of John Rogers at the stake was Richard's favorite.

Just then their father entered the room.

"Are you almost finished with Richard and Joseph?" he asked Lydia. "We'll need quiet when I hear Jemima's and John's catechism. The Reverend Hobart may call here tomorrow and wish to hear it. I want them to be well prepared. Then we'll have the Scripture reading, prayers, and go to bed."

Jemima groaned. "I know my catechism perfectly," she told Lydia. "Parson Hobart will be pleased with me, but I don't think John has studied his since Father last heard it."

"Never mind John's catechism," admonished Mr. Longley. "Look to your own faults and virtues, Jemima. I'll attend to John's."

As was customary in Puritan families, a chapter of the Bible was read aloud each evening. Starting with the first book, the entire Bible was read until the end. Then another cycle was started. Each evening the family listened to Holy Writ, taking turns reading as they grew proficient enough to sound out the difficult words. It was Will's turn to read aloud this evening, and he read from the Book of Deuteronomy, Chapter 11, verses 1–32.

As he completed the final verse—"And ye shall observe to do all the statutes and judgments which I set before you this day"—the children sat as still as mice.

"Let us pray," said their father and bowed his head solemnly as they all recited the familiar words of the Lord's Prayer.

"Good night, children," he said pleasantly at the end of the prayer. "It's time for you to go to bed."

Quietly Betty rose from Lydia's lap where she had been sitting and kissed her father and mother. Lydia went with her to the back chamber. It was nearly seven o'clock. Joseph, Richard, and John climbed the steep stairs to the loft and soon there was quiet. Not even an occasional giggle from above disturbed the peace of the summer evening.

After Lydia had helped Betty undress and climb into the little trundle bed, she listened while her little sister repeated the prayer all the Longley children had been taught to say:

"Now I lay me down to sleep.
I pray the Lord my soul to keep.
If I should die before I awake,
I pray the Lord my soul to take.
Amen."

Then Lydia returned to the kitchen. Will and his father were sitting on the doorstep making plans for the next day's work. Deliverance was preparing the mush for breakfast. Soon Jemima went off to bed, and before nine o'clock the whole family had retired. The house was still.

When Lydia slipped back into the darkened chamber, Jemima was still awake. Lydia could

barely make out the white face on the pillow as she
stooped over the trundle bed beside the larger one to
pull some light covering over Betty's sleeping figure.

"Why aren't you asleep?" whispered Lydia to
Jemima as she slipped on her long white nightgown.

"I've been lying here thinking," answered Jemima softly. "John Shepley told Will today when
they were haying that the militia will soon be having
Training Day. Won't that be exciting?"

"I hope Father will let us go. He'll let the boys go
anyway, and I am glad for them. They enjoy seeing
the soldiers march and shoot. It will give them something to look forward to. They don't get away from
the farm very often, except to meeting." She
thought of John's wish to be an Indian.

"Soon there'll be a quilting bee for us to go to,
Lydia," said Jemima, as her older sister slid into bed
and lay quietly on her back, staring up at the beams
in the darkness. "We always have fun at quiltings,
don't we? We'll hear all the news."

"Yes, it is fun," answered Lydia softly. "Listen,
Jemima," she whispered. "Hear how clear the
whippoorwills sound tonight. They're noisier than
usual, I think." Both girls held their breath as the

haunting cry of the nocturnal birds reached their ears.

"They seem to be coming from all around us. I love to hear them, don't you, Jemima?"

Jemima did not answer and Lydia knew that her sister had dropped off to sleep. She, too, settled herself comfortably, pillowed her head on her arm, and drifted off.

Day was just dawning when Lydia opened her eyes. Her sisters were still sleeping soundly and she lay for a moment before jumping out of bed and dressing swiftly. She could hear her father and Deliverance moving quietly about. No sounds could be heard from the loft, but Lydia knew that Will would soon awaken. He would rouse his brothers.

Lydia looked out of the window and, breathing deeply, drank in the fresh, pure, country air. The corn looks almost ready to pick, she thought, as she glanced casually at the fenced-in cornfield. The sun was beginning to rise in the east.

She washed herself quickly and, by the time she was back in the kitchen, Will was downstairs. He was standing in the open doorway.

"The cows are in the cornfield, Father. How could they have gotten out of the barn?" Will asked.

"They weren't there a few minutes ago when I looked out," Lydia murmured as Mr. Longley rushed to the window. "That's strange!"

Leaving the milk pails he was getting ready to take outside, he ran to the door. "Come, Will, let's catch them and put them back into the barn at once."

"John," shouted Will as he ran to the door. "The cows are out. Get up and help us catch them."

Suddenly Lydia heard bloodcurdling screams, and her heart seemed to turn over. The piercing sounds of Indian war whoops rent the air.

3.

Between Two Worlds

Standing motionless in the window, Lydia watched the frightful scene outside. For a second the thought of the noisy warning of the whippoor-wills the night before flashed through her mind.

Indians hideous with slashes of red, black, and white paint on their faces seemed to be every-where—brandishing tomahawks, firing guns, shout-ing and gesticulating. Dressed in deerskin loincloths, their greasy bodies shone in the sun. She knew that her father and Will were unarmed. Her terrified glance took in the tragic episode.

Her father fell to the ground first—dead, no doubt. She watched Will struggle with one of the savages before he was brutally felled by a swift blow on the head from the tomahawk of another Indian.

"God help us," cried Deliverance, rushing to the bedroom and snatching the baby into her arms. The savages were now running toward the house.

Lydia spun around. If I can only get my gun, she thought, as she faced Jemima coming from the back bedroom trembling. But all hope of self-defense vanished when little Betty, screaming and clutching her beloved wooden doll, flung herself at Lydia. She gathered the panic-stricken child into her arms.

"The cellar," sobbed Deliverance, trying in vain to bolt the front door as a swarm of painted savages began pouring into the kitchen, shattering walls and smashing furniture with axes and tomahawks.

Lydia would never forget Jemima's piercing screams as her sister was scalped by a cruel feathered red man with glittering eyes.

As Lydia sank to the floor in panic, she heard the

thud of falling bodies, screams, sobs. Betty's little arms still clung to her.

Suddenly an Indian was standing over them uttering guttural sounds as he raised his hatchet over Betty's tiny blond head. "Stop! I beg of you—stop!" screamed Lydia. She shielded the child with her arms and looked imploringly at the savage.

"You come north with us," he told her in grunts. "She too small." He pointed to Betty.

"I'll come," Lydia nodded in desperation. "Only let me bring her, too. I'll take care of her."

Two other savages joined Lydia's assailant. One seemed to be the leader. He nodded. Lydia and Betty stood up. The men pushed them roughly into a corner. The one who remained on guard pointed his gun menacingly at Lydia whenever she moved.

Dazedly she looked around the ruins which the murderers had effected in so short a time. The little half-dressed figures of Richard and Joseph lay on the floor in a heap. Deliverance and the baby were dead, too. To Lydia's surprise she saw three Indians holding John, who was still alive and bravely grasping his rifle.

She heard the leader say, "He go to New France

with girls. Brave boy—like Indian boy." The red
men seized John's rifle and pushed him toward the
corner where Lydia and Betty crouched. He offered no resistance, but his frightened gaze pleaded
with them for kindness.

Three of us left to live . . . only three of us
alive. This fact kept pounding in Lydia's terrified
thoughts. What will they do to us in New France?
Why haven't they killed us as they have the others?

Working hastily, the savages destroyed whatever
they didn't put to one side for themselves. Unable
to bear watching the appalling destruction of her
family home, Lydia closed her eyes for a moment.

An Indian grabbed her arm and said tersely,
"Come. Get clothes for little girl, boots for yourself.
Dress for long walk. You, too," he added to John.

At gun-point Lydia and John crossed the kitchen
to get their clothes and then, still guarded, rejoined
the Indians.

The first floor of the house was now in ruins,
stripped of everything useful. Several Indians had
brought up from the cellar armloads of supplies and
food.

"Come," was the brief command as the pathetic
procession paraded out of the narrow doorway.

Lydia could not bear to glance back, even once, at the sorrowful scene behind her.

"Dear God," she prayed silently, "have mercy on us."

With tear-filled eyes Lydia followed her captors. She held Betty tightly in her arms and motioned John to keep close to her. He watched the activities of the Indians curiously.

"Look, Lydia," he whispered, tugging at her sleeve, "they've taken all our guns, and our food, and even some of our clothing!"

One of the savages ordered them to halt, and they waited for the red men to divide the plunder among themselves. An Indian sentry stood scanning the horizon.

They worked quickly. One of the men thrust a huge piece of salted meat into John's hands.

"You carry," he grunted briefly. He cast a swift glance at Lydia as if to decide what more she could take, but turned away.

"Dear Lord, give me the strength to carry Betty and keep her safe," Lydia breathed softly.

Soon they were ready to leave. Lydia sobbed as they were led to the rear of the house and past the lifeless bodies of her father and Will. She shielded Betty's face from the tragic sight.

The Indians, loping along effortlessly, motioned Lydia and John to walk more quickly. She had all she could do to keep up with them. Betty cried piteously and called for her mother.

They strode across the fields sweet with the scent of new-mown hay and reached the woods on the other side of the Longley place not far from the main road. Any hope that aid might come from the garrison house dimmed as Lydia looked hesitantly backward. No one was in sight.

"Where are we going?" asked Betty, still holding her precious doll. "Are the Indians taking us for a walk?"

"Hush, dear," whispered Lydia. "I don't know where they are taking us, but let's be just as quiet as we can be." Her muscles were already beginning to ache, despite the fact that the child was frail and small.

On the edge of the wood John stopped short and cried, "Snowball! She's shut up in the barn with the other sheep and will starve. I must let her out!"

Lydia was paralyzed with fear as one of the warriors pushed John along.

"Go on—don't stop," he muttered with an ugly expression in his eyes. "Get along!"

"No," persisted the boy. "I must let our sheep out of the barn. They'll starve."

The ten savages stopped short and turned to the youngster. They muttered a few unintelligible words and gestured violently, looking toward the village. For some reason Lydia felt they would listen to John. Perhaps animals were more important to them than human beings.

"I'll come back to you, I promise," said the boy, solemnly holding up his right hand.

The leader looked at John searchingly, then nodded and waved him toward the barn. The Indians whose packs were not strapped on their shoulders laid them down on the ground. The guard nearest Lydia motioned her to rest as John started on the run across the fields. She dropped down on the pine needles with Betty beside her and stared at the flying figure of her brother. If only someone would come down the road and see him, perhaps they could yet be saved!

But no such miracle happened. The boy reached the barn, opened the door, and a line of sheep walked out.

Lydia knew there was no point in hoping that John would dart off down the road in search of help. He had promised to return and he would. Besides, a well-aimed bullet would soon put an end to him if he made any such foolhardy attempt.

"See John hugging Snowball," said Betty, pointing toward home, and Lydia watched sadly as her brother said a final good-by to his pet.

What will the future hold for the three of us? she wondered fearfully as she drew the little one closer. The Indians were staring expressionlessly at the boy now returning to them.

In no time he was back, puffing and out of breath.

"Thank you," he said to the grim-faced savages. "Snowball will be all right now. Someone will find her and take care of her. I'll miss her, though," he said, turning to Lydia, his eyes filling with tears and his lips quivering. "But I said good-by to her. She won't forget me."

"Come," said one of the guards. "Hurry. Have far to go."

It seemed hours before they stopped again. Part of the time Lydia carried Betty, and sometimes John shared the burden while she took his load. Although the Indians seemed to be following a def-

inite route, in many places the bushes were thick
and difficult to penetrate. The sun was climbing
higher in the sky, and Lydia's strength was beginning to give out.

She could feel her feet swelling. Black flies bit
her and the children incessantly. Betty sobbed in
misery, and Lydia's heart ached for the little girl.
It dawned on her that they had eaten nothing since
the early supper of the afternoon before. Betty
began to beg for a drink. Even John was showing
signs of strain and fatigue.

Suddenly they came upon a brook and, to Lydia's
great relief, the Indians stopped. Without waiting
for permission, she sank to the ground in exhaustion.
John ran to the stream, followed by the guard
whose captive he evidently was. All of the Indians
knelt and scooped up water in their palms, drinking
at the wrists as was their custom.

Lydia and Betty stumbled over to the brook and
drank, dabbing their faces with the refreshing
water.

"I can't carry Betty much farther," panted Lydia
anxiously to John. She spoke very softly so as not to
be heard by the Indians. "What shall we do?" she

asked desperately, as the howl of an animal sounded menacingly close.

To her surprise the Indians repeated the call that had seemed so like a wild beast's, and soon a band of thirty or more braves joined their party.

"Look," whispered John. "See the packs piled over there by those bushes? This must be their meeting place."

Lydia realized then that their attackers were just a small part of a larger band of Indians. Perhaps the attack on Groton had been more widespread than she had imagined. Other families must have been killed, too.

"Why, there's John Shepley, all bound up!" exclaimed John. "And the Hobart boy, and . . ." He started to name others, but an Indian motioned him to keep still and brandished a tomahawk at him.

The Longleys watched a big muscular Indian chief step to the center of the clearing and hold up his hands for silence. They couldn't understand much of what he said, but it was evident that he gave orders about the march and about the captives, for he pointed to them.

Exhausted as she was, Lydia had enough presence of mind to count the other prisoners. There were ten besides themselves—mostly children she knew, only half-dressed and with terror-stricken faces. Most of them were crying.

The warriors seemed to remain in their own little group and soon began to fasten the packs on their backs by means of carrying straps across the forehead. The Indian chief gave the signal, and they roused their prisoners into formation. The same two men guarded Lydia, Betty, and John. One of them strapped a pack on Lydia's back, then picked up Betty, and led the way forward.

Lydia started to protest, then restrained herself. She realized that it was the only solution. She couldn't have carried Betty much longer. The little girl's face was livid with fear, but Lydia motioned her to remain quiet.

"You'll be all right, dear," she whispered. "I'm right behind you, and he can carry you more easily then I can."

She and John toiled on, endlessly, it seemed, until the Indians themselves must have wished to eat, for at length the entire band halted in a grove.

The sun was high. It must be noon, Lydia thought. She and John sat down to rest, Betty between them. The men unpacked the plunder stolen from Groton and started to devour the food. They threw scraps to the captives, which John grabbed and shared with Betty. Lydia refused to touch it. It sickened her. The shock of the morning's horrible experience was beginning to have its effect. Her stomach rebelled, despite the need for nourishment.

Her feet pained, her skirt was torn, and her bleeding legs had been cut by ragged branches. Perspiration ran in a stream down her mosquito-bitten cheeks; her hair was matted. Seeing some checkerberries close by, she remembered the walk she had taken into the woods with John. He talked of wanting to be an Indian, thought Lydia bitterly. Could it have been only yesterday? It seemed years ago.

Betty's face was tear-streaked and woebegone. She had tired of carrying her doll and had handed it to Lydia. As Lydia looked at her, she was once more filled with dread and anxiety for her little sister's well-being.

One of the braves approached the three and handed them pieces of corn bread and scraps of salted meat.

"Water over there," he directed. John ate ravenously and ran over to the water. Lydia half pulled, half carried Betty to the stream and splashed their faces. They lay down like animals and lapped the water. Lydia then forced herself to eat.

The march continued. As they plodded along through woods and clearings, they heard feeble cries. Lydia guessed that some of the captives had given out and been killed. Since the long line was divided into separate groups, each Indian claiming his own captives, she could not see what happened to the others. She constantly feared for Betty's life, but the savage carrying her seemed tireless.

John, who had lagged behind Lydia to talk with the other guard, caught up with her.

"My guard's name is Black Eagle," he said. "And the big chief's called Taxous."

Lydia marveled that John could bring himself to carry on a conversation with these savages.

"They live in an Indian village on the Penobscot River," John went on. "Black Eagle says it's in Acadia. Lucky for me that he can speak English. He says they're Abenaki Indians." He stumbled over the pronunciation of the difficult name.

"What else did he tell you?" asked Lydia.

"They're taking us to Ville-Marie in New France and plan to sell us to the French people for lots of money," John replied. "What do you sup-

pose the French people are like? I wish I could stay
with the Indians. I know I'd get used to living out-
of-doors most of the time. I'd get strong like they
are."

"You're bewitched with these murderers!"
Lydia exclaimed angrily. "How can you even think
such a thing, let alone say it?"

Hours passed and the party came to a river. Lydia
supposed it must be the Merrimac. Once more they
halted and campfires were built. They were given
a little food—not much, just nuts and small bits of
salted meat. Evidently the food stolen at Groton
was gone.

The itching of the insect bites was unbearable.
Their faces were swollen beyond recognition, and
Betty continually uttered sorrowful little cries.

If only there were some milk for her, Lydia
wished, but she dared not ask the Indians for a thing
lest they kill the child.

John helped the braves pile mounds of leafy
branches that they had cut from the bushes to make
beds around the campfires. Among themselves the
Indians were noisy, but finally they tossed some
skins to Lydia and John, wrapped themselves up,
and slept, feet toward the fire.

Momentarily Lydia had considered escape, but fear of their captors and of wild animals in the dark forests all about them soon made her give up any such plans. She wrapped Betty more tightly in her shawl and lay down close beside her. It was damp by the river as the fires dimmed. The little girl coughed and Lydia pulled the corners of the deer-skin around her. John, rolled up in his own deerskin, was fast asleep.

By morning Lydia knew that Betty was seriously ill. Her face was burning with fever, yet she complained of being cold. The older girl saw John looking at his little sister with concern as she whimpered. Then he turned away to watch the activity all about them.

"See where they hid their canoes," he said to Lydia, pointing to the Indians carefully loading the boats which they had removed from behind the thick foliage along the shore.

"Yes," she replied. "They evidently left them here before they attacked Groton."

She looked anxiously down at little Betty whose heavy breathing and constant coughing made Lydia dread the hours of travel ahead of them. For a minute she pictured the nourishing breakfast they were used to eating at home—the warm porridge and milk—and shivered in the chill of the early morning dampness. Even though it was July, it was cold at daybreak.

They were on their way shortly after dawn, this time in canoes. For the first time since they had left home, John was separated from his sisters. Black Eagle motioned him into a canoe which he pushed off at once. Lydia soon lost sight of it.

There were thirty or more canoes in all, and it was difficult to distinguish one from another. The black-haired savages all looked alike to the girl as she watched them paddling swiftly up the stream. She wished she knew the name of the Indian who had captured her, but he was a silent, surly-looking person who never spoke unless he had a command to give.

She cradled Betty in her arms and from time to time changed position. Her muscles were aching and her legs cramped, but she must bear the pain, for she had to keep the sick child close to her.

The day seemed endless. Lydia lost track of time in her concern for Betty, who had become worse and now seemed almost lifeless.

At nightfall they again made camp, and the

warmth from the fires seemed more than welcome. Lydia smelled broiling meat and her mouth watered, but none was given to her or to John. They had been given only a few berries when they left the boat and some bark to chew on. John ran over to his sisters as soon as he could.

"How is she?" he asked Lydia anxiously as they looked at the little form wrapped in the shawl.

Lydia shook her head. Hungry, weak, and cold, she forced herself to stay awake as long as she could that night, but finally she dropped off, arms drawn protectively about her little sister.

The next morning Betty did not stir. Lydia knew at once that she was dead. Dazed by sorrow, worry, and fear, she did not dare ask the Indians to bury the child. She and John kissed the cold little face and covered the tiny body with the shawl.

"We must say the Lord's Prayer, John," she whispered weakly, bowing her head and repeating with him the familiar words. "Perhaps, we, too, will die like this," she sobbed.

Leaving the beloved doll tucked under the folds of the coverlet, they followed their cruel captors down to the water's edge. Not one of the savages had even commented on Betty's death.

This time Lydia and John were told to use the same canoe with their guards, and for this Lydia was thankful. John seemed stronger than she.

"Black Eagle let me paddle part of the way yesterday," he informed her. "He showed me how to do it. I could have done better if I hadn't been so hungry," he added.

"Black Eagle seems to be kinder than the others," Lydia said softly. "We should be thankful for that."

Hours and days passed, one much like the next. Lydia lost all sense of time or direction. Numb and unseeing, she dragged herself along on land when they traveled cross-country and stumbled into the canoes when bidden to do so. Sometimes the streams were rocky and shallow. At other times the Indians could hardly guide their canoes through swamps filled with waterweeds and alders.

There were days when neither the Indians nor their captives had much to eat. Both Lydia and John were expected to carry packs when toiling over hills, rocky paths, and along the forest trails, for the two Indians were carrying the empty canoe on their shoulders. There were times when Lydia wished herself dead. Occasionally she stumbled and fell to the ground. John would help her up almost against her will.

"You must keep going, Lydia," he urged. "Perhaps we'll be given more food soon. Black Eagle may shoot a deer."

After several more days of wearisome travel, they came upon an expanse of shining water.

"This Petonque. White man call it Lake Champlain," Black Eagle informed them. "Soon we come to Abenaki village at St. Francis where I stay for a while," he grunted haltingly.

"Where will we go?" asked John eagerly.

"You stay with me. She go to Ville-Marie. Your name John Augary."

Lydia could scarcely grasp what he meant, but later she began to realize that John and Black Eagle were leaving her. Weak as she was, she clung to John.

"Good-by, Lydia," her brother said, putting his arms about her neck and hugging her. "I hope we'll see each other again."

"Good-by, John," she sobbed. "Our Father in heaven alone knows what will become of us."

But her Indian guard thrust her from the boy's embrace and hurried her to the waiting canoe. She

tottered into it, dimly aware that the two of them
were traveling alone.

She sank into a semiconscious state of melan-
choly. Numbed by the tragic circumstances and
lack of nourishment, Lydia ceased to realize what
was happening. Time stopped.

Much, much later she dreamed she saw a kind,
white-haired gentleman approaching and speaking
gently to her. He seemed to guide her away from
her captor to a house and a room and a clean white
bed where she sank finally into blessed sleep.

4.

RANSOMED

Lydia stirred restlessly in her sleep. She fancied she could hear the meetinghouse bell sounding clear and loud. Someone must be warning the people of Groton of an Indian attack. She sat up suddenly. The bells continued to ring close by, and Lydia could hear the sound of footsteps passing. She rubbed her eyes and looked about bewildered.

In a flash she remembered the cruel attack and the weary days of travel with the savages. But her mind was blank after a certain point. How did I get here? she wondered.

The bed in which she lay was soft and comfortable. She touched the smooth linen sheets with appreciation and laid her cheek against the silky-soft pale blue coverlet drawn over her.

The room was more luxurious than any she had ever seen. Its walls were a deep blue, and at the casement windows hung pale pink draperies. The dark furniture was rich looking. Close by the bed stood two chairs upholstered in rose-colored velvet.

Lydia's gaze was drawn to a picture on the wall facing her. It was an exquisite oil painting of a mother and Child with a halo about His head, done in soft colors which harmonized with the surroundings. The compassionate eyes of the mother seemed to be looking straight at Lydia with sympathy and understanding.

"It must be Jesus and Mary," breathed the girl softly. "I've never seen anything so beautiful. She seems almost alive."

Lydia covered her face with her hands and lay back on the down pillow, stifling her sobs. A feeling of aloneness swept over her. How could she face the future without her family? How could she live without her father and mother and her dear brothers and sisters? All gone, all dead—except John. . . . John. She repeated his name to herself, wondering where he was at that moment. Somewhere out in the forest roaming with the Indians? She shuddered.

As Lydia sat up once more, she realized that she was stiff and lame. Again she looked about the room. A tiny vase of flowers stood before a statue on a shelf in one corner. Turning, she noticed a silver cross on the wall directly over her head. Outlined on it was the figure of Christ hanging in agony, His Hands and Feet nailed, and around His sorrowful, drooping Head a crown of thorns. The sight of it repelled her!

"Jesus on the Cross," she whispered, staring with a strange fascination. "Why should people want that in a room to remind them constantly of His sufferings?"

Again she heard the peal of church bells, and a sudden thought gripped her. "I'm in the home of French Papists!" she exclaimed in horror. "What will they do to me? I'm English—and they are our enemies."

Throwing back the bedclothes, she made an

effort to get up. She discovered that her legs were bandaged with soft white cloths and that she was so weak she could barely stand on the thickly carpeted floor.

She was clothed in a white nightgown which fell in soft folds about her, its yoke daintily embroidered, its neck and sleeves bordered with exquisite handmade lace. The clothes she had worn on the journey were nowhere about. Her arms were covered with the disfiguring marks and scars of insect bites. A wave of dizziness enveloped her and she sank back on the bed from sheer exhaustion.

At that moment the door was opened quietly and Lydia saw a middle-aged woman wearing a black dress and white apron staring at her in pleased surprise. Her friendly face and greying hair were framed in a sheer white cap.

Lydia smiled as the woman held up her hands in amazement and uttered little cries of joy, but the girl couldn't understand the torrent of words which followed. She talked constantly as she helped Lydia bathe face and hands and brought mirror and comb to her. Then the woman wrapped a finely woven blue woolen dressing gown about Lydia's shoulders and left the room.

When she returned, she carried a tray on which was a steaming cup of hot chocolate, slices of freshly baked bread, and wild strawberry conserve. The aroma of the chocolate was tantalizing, and Lydia realized how hungry she was. She wondered when she had last eaten. She had no recollection of coming to this house, no memory of having seen this woman before. But with girlish appetite she ate every morsel.

A knock sounded on the door, and her new friend appeared, accompanied by a grey-haired gentleman in his early sixties. He was dressed in a dark blue coat and light breeches. Close behind him was a younger man, tall and handsome, in a flowing black garment. Lydia drew her robe more closely about her as they approached the bed and regarded her with smiles of interest.

The older man spoke haltingly. "*Ma petite*, do not fear us. We will not harm you. I am Jacques LeBer and this is Monsieur Meriel, our good priest at the Hotel-Dieu, our hospital."

Touching the woman on the arm, he said, "This is Madame Dupont, my housekeeper. Madame Le-Ber, my wife, is dead these past twelve years."

To Lydia's surprise, he touched his forehead, chest, and two shoulders in the sign of a cross.

The housekeeper smiled a greeting and left the room silently. Lydia bowed her head as she acknowledged the introductions. Monsieur Meriel bent over to shake her thin white hand and she noticed his purple cuffs against the black of his robe. This is a Papist priest, she thought, but he seems kind.

Monsieur LeBer continued in his halting English. "I do not speak your language well, but Monsieur Meriel does speak well and will tell you many things you wish to know." His brown eyes were kind and his gaze direct as he looked at her. He sat down on one of the velvet chairs and Lydia noticed the lace at his wrists as he motioned to his companion to take the other. His elegant clothes were a startling contrast to the plain, dark simplicity of Puritan attire back in Groton.

"You have been very ill for many days," said the priest, "but you are young, and doubtless strong, and will soon be completely well again. You are fortunate, indeed, my dear girl, to be under the protection of Monsieur LeBer. He has taken you as his ward and will be your guardian from now on. Can you remember how you reached Ville-Marie?"

"So I *am* in the city of Ville-Marie," said Lydia hesitatingly. "The Indians said they were taking me here."

"Yes," answered the young priest. "You certainly are in Ville-Marie in New France. No doubt you have undergone terrible experiences. You must try to forget them. The war between England and France, which started six years ago when William of Orange came to the throne of England, has brought about unfortunate conditions. We have other English captives here, also ransomed from the Indians. And in Boston there are French prisoners whom your English people have captured and are holding. It is a tragic situation. Luckily for you, Monsieur LeBer is a kind and generous man, well respected in Ville-Marie, and a devout Catholic. You will be treated like a daughter."

"I thank you, sir," said Lydia softly, turning to the older man. "I am indebted to you for the care I have received. I hope I will be allowed to show my appreciation to you in some manner."

Monsieur LeBer shook his head—sadly, it seemed to Lydia—but did not appear to understand what she had said.

The priest explained, "He is a lonely man. His

wife gone—may they meet in heaven; his son, Jean, killed in battle with the English and the Iroquois three years ago; two other sons now in France, and only Pierre left at home. But God has been good to him in other ways. He has made a great deal of money in the fur trade. He is an immensely wealthy man."

"Has he no daughters, sir?" asked Lydia.

Monsieur Meriel was silent for a moment and turned to Monsieur LeBer who was leaning forward. "One," he replied, slowly and thoughtfully. "She is here in the house and I will tell you about her one day soon. She is a living saint, but it is difficult for her father to understand the will of God."

Lydia was puzzled. Monsieur Meriel patted the older man's arm in a comforting gesture and then turned again to the girl.

"I must now ask you questions for our record. Do you understand your situation?"

"No, sir, I do not," she answered. "Am I a prisoner in this country?"

Monsieur Meriel hesitated momentarily. "Let me explain to you more fully. War in Europe means, unfortunately, war in the colonies. There are many problems here in this new country. Trade supremacy is one. Our relationship to the Indians is another. The lands of Acadia are a third. Both nations are fighting for control of Acadia. The English are in league with the Iroquois and the Abenakis are friendly to us because the English mishandled them while they were in power. At present, we have control of Acadia." He sighed and continued.

"In time you may be returned to your country, or you may find so much happiness in this land of our Blessed Mother that you will choose to remain with us. Who knows? Only the good God!" He shrugged his shoulders. "But you will find much to occupy yourself. And now, please, what is your name and where were you born?" Monsieur Meriel walked over to a little desk in one corner of the chamber and sat down to write.

"I am Lydia Longley, born in Groton in New England," answered the girl solemnly.

"Are you willing to tell us what happened to you and where you were taken captive by the Indians?" the priest questioned.

Lydia's eyes filled with tears. "It was on the morning of July 27, shortly after dawn. The savages attacked our home, killed my father and my step-mother, Deliverance Crisp, four of my brothers, and one sister. They took my brother, John, my little sister, Betty, and me as prisoners. Betty died on the journey. They have kept John with them— and I am here, sir," she finished simply. "I don't know how I got here—to this house, sir." She turned to Monsieur LeBer, who was listening closely.

"I can answer that," said Monsieur Meriel. "Monsieur LeBer was in the office of the intendant, the official who is the head of our civil government, when the Abenaki brought you in half dead, dragging you almost senseless through the doorway. Monsieur LeBer has a big heart and gladly paid your ransom. He had you brought here to his home."

How different this Papist priest is from what I might have imagined, thought Lydia. And what a wonderful man Monsieur LeBer must be! I should learn to speak his language so that I can thank him properly.

She supplied Monsieur Meriel with other details which he recorded in exquisite handwriting.

Monsieur LeBer interrupted them with a flow of French directed at the priest.

"The dressmaker who served Madame LeBer will come soon to fit you with suitable clothing, Lydia," explained the priest kindly, "and Monsieur LeBer will speak to Jean St. Pierre, the cobbler, about measuring your feet for shoes. You will like some pretty slippers with red heels which the ladies are wearing, I'm sure," he added, his kind eyes twinkling. "And these moccasins here are for your use in the meantime." He bent to the floor at the foot of her bed and held up a pair of beautifully beaded moccasins.

"Will it be proper for me to wear shoes with red heels, sir?" asked Lydia doubtfully. "We Puritans of Groton were not allowed to dress in bright colors."

"You are now in New France, my child," said Monsieur Meriel. "The French ladies are very stylish and like pretty colors. You will wish to dress according to your station as Monsieur LeBer's ward so long as you are modestly clothed and appear ladylike and proper."

"I see," answered Lydia, feeling a trifle guilty that she enjoyed the thoughts of slippers with red heels.

"The lay nurses who have been attending to your needs under the direction of the hospital sisters will continue their care until you are able to be up and about," said Monsieur Meriel, as he carefully placed Lydia's record sheet in an envelope.

"And whose sisters may they be?" asked Lydia curiously.

"Have you never seen sisters?" he asked.

Lydia shook her head.

"Many young ladies of our religious faith, through the grace of God, offer their lives to His service. Sister Jeanne Mance, now dead, established the Hotel-Dieu where the sisters nurse the sick of the colony and care for the poor. From your window here, if you look closely, you can see the vigil lamp burning in their chapel at the hospital. These sisters work cheerfully for the glory of God. As Monsieur LeBer told you, I am their chaplain. At the convent other sisters work as uncloistered missionaries under the direction of Mother Bourgeoys. They instruct the girls of New France and teach them to love God and serve Him by living a Christian life."

I am in a completely new world, thought Lydia, so different from Groton. Yet these gentlemen are good men and kind to me.

"You understand, Lydia," the priest was saying, "they can never marry. Their lives are entirely devoted to God. They take vows of poverty, chastity, and obedience.

"We priests of the Sulpician Order also devote ourselves to gaining souls for God and Holy Mother the Church and administering the sacraments to the faithful. We never marry, as do your Puritan ministers, for we believe family life would divert our interests from duty to our people."

"I know nothing of such things, sir," said Lydia respectfully. "I have never before met Papists, but I shall be glad to see these sisters as well as the nurses and thank them for what they have done in my behalf. Do they speak English?"

"I know of none who do," said Monsieur Meriel, "and I am the only priest in Ville-Marie who can speak your language. However, there is a young English girl of thirteen, named Mary Genevieve Sayer, who attends school at the convent and is deeply attached to the sisters. She will talk with you in English."

"Would you like to speak French?" asked Monsieur LeBer hesitatingly, with a self-conscious smile. He gestured to clarify his words. "The sisters could teach you."

Lydia's eyes shone. "I would certainly enjoy that,

sir," she nodded. "I would study diligently. I like to
learn. I used to teach my younger brothers to read
and write and do their sums. And I'd especially like
to meet the English girl."

Monsieur Meriel stood up. "You look fatigued,
Lydia. I must return to the Hotel-Dieu and you
should try to sleep. We will all help you to forget
the trials you have suffered. Remember that He, too,
suffered for us and died on the Cross. Perhaps some
day you may find comfort in our Church and be
resigned to your fate in our midst. Another more
saintly than we may be your guide."

Lydia was puzzled. "Another more saintly than
we . . ."

Monsieur LeBer rose and spoke in French to the
priest. Monsieur Meriel turned to Lydia and said,
"You must not hesitate to call upon Monsieur LeBer
when he is in the house. His fur business takes him
away sometimes. I will call on you soon again. In a
short time you will be able to go downstairs and
meet Pierre LeBer, who will show you about Ville-
Marie. Perhaps Pierre's cousin, Anne Barroy, who
spends part of each day in this house, will accom-
pany you. Rest, my child, for the present." The
two gentlemen left the room together.

Days and weeks passed quickly as the girl captive from Groton became accustomed to her new world. Sometimes she was haunted by thoughts of the Indians. There were nightmares in which she was pursued by cruel savages brandishing tomahawks; she would awaken, wet with perspiration and fear. Little by little the nightmares became less frequent, as did her moods of depression and homesickness. Lydia slowly gained back her strength and vitality. One of her greatest sources of comfort was the beautiful painting of the mother and Child facing her bed.

Before long she was spending hours at her window watching the activity in the street below. Little boys playing soldiers and Indians reminded her of her own brothers. Small girls dressed in grey cloaks and carrying baskets passed the house each day on their way to school. Sometimes long lines of them paraded past, accompanied by women in long black robes whom Lydia realized must be Catholic sisters. The gentlemen who walked by wore three-cornered hats and long-tailed blue coats, a color which she later learned was the distinguishing mark of Ville-Marie, just as men wore red coats in Quebec and white in Three Rivers.

She was told that the LeBer home was on Rue St. Joseph, near the intersection with Rue St. Paul, the main thoroughfare. She could see across to the Hotel-Dieu, and not far away were the school buildings of the Congregation de Notre Dame, Mother Bourgeoys' community of sisters.

She could look off in the distance to the palisades of Ville-Marie and the great St. Lawrence River. On it shallops—little boats with one sail—and larger river barges plied to and fro. Madame Dupont told her the names of the streets and buildings. She looked forward to the day when she would be strong enough to walk about in the quaint foreign settlement so different from Groton.

She was astonished at how quickly she learned to understand French. Surrounded by people who couldn't speak English, she was forced to make a great effort to understand what they said.

Gentle nurses from the Hotel-Dieu came to change her bandages and apply ointment to her insect bites and infections, but soon their services were no longer necessary. Lydia's skin healed quickly. It would be much later before the mental shock and physical weakness would be a thing of the past.

Both Monsieur LeBer and Monsieur Meriel felt that learning French would help to divert Lydia and keep her active mind from dwelling on the tragedy of the past. A young sister from Mother Bourgeoys' congregation came to her room to teach her. Much later, Lydia continued her lessons at the convent school until she could express herself clearly in French and could read and write the language.

The sweet face and charming manners of the sister who visited her appealed to Lydia's natural love of refinement, but her clothing seemed strange to the girl who had never before seen Catholic nuns. She learned that each group had its own distinguishing habit. The young sister of the congregation who came to teach Lydia wore a long black robe belted about the waist, a dark veil over a white linen head-dress which outlined her face, a snow-white necker-chief, and a large cross like the one above Lydia's bed.

One day Madame Dupont ushered in an elderly nun and a young girl whom she introduced as Mother Bourgeoys and Mary Genevieve Sayer, captive from York. Ever since Monsieur Meriel had told Lydia about the foundress and the English girl, she had longed to meet them.

Lydia was instantly attracted to the woman whose goodness seemed to shine from her dark eyes. Mother Bourgeoys clasped the girl's hand and gazed at her with sympathy and understanding.

"My dear child, we at the convent have thought of you often and prayed for your recovery. You have improved since I saw you last." She smiled. "You didn't know I looked in on you several times when you were so very ill, did you?"

Lydia shook her head in surprise. How straight the ruddy-cheeked sister stood, despite her advanced age! Mother Bourgeoys turned to include Mary Genevieve in the conversation.

"Monsieur LeBer and I felt that you would like to meet another English girl—a captive like yourself—and Mary Genevieve has been most anxious to see you. You have much in common, unfortunately."

"I'm so glad to meet you," said the younger girl in English. She held out a little package and added, "We have brought you these tiny gifts."

Lydia's eyes filled with unrestrained tears as she opened the package to find a little pincushion and a picture of the Infant Jesus.

"I made the pincushion at school," said Mary

Genevieve shyly, "and the holy picture is from Mother Bourgeoys. It came from France."

They smiled as Lydia thanked them and then placed the presents on a table close by so that she could look at them from time to time. Lydia learned that Mary Genevieve had been captured by the Indians two years before, along with her mother and sister. They lived with a kind widow, and the two girls attended school at the convent.

"I love it, too!" exclaimed the girl. "I never went to school before. The sisters are so good to me." She turned a look of gratitude upon Mother Bourgeoys. "I'm going to be a sister when I'm old enough to enter. I'm thirteen, now." Mary Genevieve's face glowed as she talked about the nuns.

"I have become a Catholic," the girl from York continued. "Mother and Esther, too. We have been so happy here in Ville-Marie! I received my first Holy Communion last December—and made all my preparation in French! Our name in English is Sayward, but the people here in New France call it Sayer."

"It is strange how quickly one learns to speak French and to understand it," replied Lydia. "I'm surprised at myself!"

"You are living with a fine family, Lydia. Monsieur LeBer is well known throughout New France. He has the reputation of being one of the most honest fur traders in the country. He has been kind to other English captives and is generous to everybody, especially to the Church. Have you seen his daughter Jeanne? People call her the recluse."

Lydia shook her head. "I know nothing of Mademoiselle LeBer, except that she is in the house. She is never in sight when my door is open."

Mary Genevieve hesitated and lowered her voice. "I've seen her at Mass. She stays in her room alone, except for her cousin, Anne Barroy, and prays. The sisters say she is a living saint, and Mother Bourgeoys comes here to see her once in a while. Maybe Monsieur Meriel will tell you something about her and will explain about saints and sacrifice. That must be confusing to you."

Monsieur Meriel's words, "Another more saintly than we," flashed through Lydia's mind. He must have been referring to Jeanne LeBer.

While the girls talked in English, Mother Bourgeoys sat watching them happily. From a pocket in the folds of her habit she had drawn a black sewing bag. Now she was knitting a half-finished sock. Lydia found herself chatting away, telling about Groton and listening to Mary Genevieve describe her experiences in Ville-Marie. She was amazed to see how content the younger girl seemed and how well she had adjusted to her new life in a strange country.

"Wouldn't you like to hear about how Mother Bourgeoys first came here and how she happened to start teaching the girls of Ville-Marie?" asked Mary Genevieve. "I'll ask her to tell you, and I'll translate what you don't understand. It's really a thrilling story."

"I'd love to hear it." Lydia felt herself drawn toward Mother Bourgeoys. The sister laid her knitting aside and leaned forward in her chair. As she spoke, Lydia watched the expressive French hands gesturing to illustrate her words. Her face is beautiful, thought the girl, serene and peaceful, yet marked with lines of age and character. She is someone I can trust—someone who can advise and help me when I need it. I can understand Mary Genevieve's devotion to her.

"The settling of our country," Mother Bourgeoys was saying, "differs from yours in that the English came to the new world principally to gain

religious freedom. But the French were happy in
their religious faith. They came here as representatives of the Church to gain more souls for God, and
they consecrated Ville-Marie to the Holy Family.

"Fifty-two years ago," she continued, "a devout
and courageous gentleman named Paul de
Maisonneuve headed the first group of men and
women who settled here. He became the first governor of Ville-Marie. This group included a beautiful woman, Jeanne Mance, foundress of the
Hotel-Dieu. Then thirty-six years old, she had de-
sired since childhood to consecrate her life to the
glory of God by service to the sick. Three other
women were here, as well as two priests, and about
forty soldiers, artisans, and colonists.

"As they left their boats on the shores of the wilderness, they sang fervent hymns of thanksgiving
and knelt in prayer. That night they slept in tents.
The next morning an altar was raised and tastefully
decorated by the women. Père Vimont, the Jesuit
priest, celebrated Mass and told the little group,
'You are a grain of mustard seed that shall rise and
grow till its branches overshadow the earth. You
are few, but your work is the work of God. His
smile is on you, and your children shall fill the land.'

"Eleven years later de Maisonneuve returned to France to interest more people in coming to the little outpost of Ville-Marie, which means in English the 'city of Mary.' Through the influence of his sister, superior of the Notre Dame Convent in Troyes, I consented to come here to teach. I was not yet a sister at that time, of course.

"When I arrived, everyone lived within the fort which included the chapel, hospital, lodgings for the colonists, and the garrison. But since there were no children old enough for instruction, it was five years before I was able to open a school. That was disappointing to me."

"Whatever did you do during those five years?" asked Lydia.

The elderly sister shook her head and sighed. "Well, I did a bit of everything. I helped mothers with their babies, washed the clothing of the soldiers, assisted both men and women with their sewing. I tried to lighten somewhat the heavy burdens of the colonists.

"I opened my first school on April 30, 1658, assisted by Marguerite Picard, who lived with me. In a little stone stable given us by de Maisonneuve we welcomed seven little boys and girls, all nine years of age or under, and began teaching them religion, writing, and arithmetic. My dream of a day school, a Sunday School, and an outside congregation or sodality modeled on one back in Troyes, came true, and our meeting place became known as 'The Congregation.' Still later my assistants and I were called 'Sisters of the Congregation' by the people of Ville-Marie. We dedicated our community to our Lady.

"My school grew, and I returned to France to invite other young women to come back with me and teach. That first visit home resulted in the coming of four girls as teachers—the beginnings of the Congregation de Notre Dame. We wore no habits and were bound by no vows, but in the eyes of the colonists we were school mistresses living a community life. The rule I drew up for our community was practical and compatible with our duties as missionary teachers. I only pray I live now to see our congregation approved by ecclesiastical authorities."

"What do you mean by that, Mother Bourgeoys?" asked Lydia curiously.

Mother Bourgeoys settled back in her chair. "You see, I have always believed that uncloistered sisters are necessary to our beloved Church, sisters who can leave the convent and go out among people, Lydia. Those of our congregation teach the children of this country, not only here in Ville-Marie, but also in Quebec, Three Rivers, and on the Isle of Orléans. We have opened schools in a number of smaller settlements, too.

"For years I have tried to procure a suitable rule for the congregation which will be acceptable to the bishop and to the pope, for only then will we be truly an order. One problem has been that the bishop finds it difficult to understand that we must be uncloistered for our particular missionary work. Now we are only lay sisters who have taken voluntary vows. Some day my dream will come true. I know that. Some day we will be established and recognized the world over as an order!"

"Oh, I hope so," said Lydia. "That's a wonderful story. I'm more anxious than ever to see your school."

Mother Bourgeoys walked to the window and the girls followed her.

"My first building was just opposite the Hotel-Dieu, over there," she explained. "You get a fine view of the school from here, and of the whole island, in fact. There must be about 1,500 people here now—quite different from my first sight of the settlement." She chuckled. "We are building a new chapel, as you can see, thanks to the gift of a saintly member of this household."

Mother Bourgeoys must be referring to Jeanne LeBer, thought Lydia. And she wondered when Monsieur Meriel would keep his promise to tell her about Monsieur LeBer's daughter.

"Mother Bourgeoys," Genevieve said, "tell Lydia about Bonsecours Church and the miraculous statue."

They sat down again and the sister continued. "Bonsecours is a church you will wish to visit many times, Lydia, I hope. From the first moment I arrived in Ville-Marie, I was filled with the desire to build a church here dedicated to our Lady. In order to do so, I decided to solicit donations from people in France when I journeyed there on business for my community. We added our own meager savings to what I collected, and finally the church was completed. It was a wonderful day for me when the first Mass was celebrated there sixteen years ago. I am happy that even its spires are a consolation to sailors approaching Ville-Marie. Many seamen have a special devotion to our Blessed Mother, Lydia, and I hope you, too, will learn to love her."

"Sometimes in the early evening we walk out and visit Bonsecours and ask special favors of our Lady," interposed Mary Genevieve. "I love to go there."

"Forgive me," said Lydia, turning to Mother Bourgeoys, "but sometimes it seems to me that you place greater faith in Mary than in Jesus. That is difficult for me to understand."

"We really do not, my dear, although our colony is dedicated to her, and we feel that the Mother of God has a special place in the heart of her Son. Perhaps we talk more about her, however. I know of many favors she has granted to those she loves. You, too, may receive special blessings when you go to Bonsecours to pray and to visit her miraculous statue."

"A miraculous statue?" Lydia was incredulous.

"It is called so, Lydia. You must understand that it is not the piece of wood, but the faith that people have in the Mother of God, and the prayers they pour out to her, that result in the wonderful good fortune she sends them. I, myself, brought the statue back from France twenty-two years ago. It was a

gift from Baron de Fancamp, one of the associates
of the Montreal Company.

"About one hundred years ago, the wood from a
tree in Montaigu, Belgium, was placed in a chapel
which had been especially built to receive it by the
Archduke Albert and his wife, Isabella. This statue
was one of three carved from that wood of the
Montaigu oak. For years it was honored by a family
named Le Pretre, but they parted with it willingly
when they knew its destination. Their only stipulation was that it should 'help animate the piety of the
people of Montreal (as Ville-Marie is sometimes
called) by honoring there the Blessed Virgin to
whom the island is dedicated and of which she is the
sovereign.'

"Now, my dear, we must go. If I can help you,
don't hesitate to call upon me. Come, Mary
Genevieve, we must leave now, but we will look
forward to seeing you, Lydia, soon. I know you and
Mary Genevieve will be good friends."

After they had gone, Lydia ran over to the window to watch the two figures—the woman in flowing black habit and the attractive girl in the grey
cloak—walking away slowly in the direction of the
convent.

Burying her face in her hands, Lydia whispered to herself, "It's difficult for me to realize what has happened. Can this be I so far from Groton—among foreign peoples—in a strange country?"

She raised her head slowly and looked out once more. The figures had almost disappeared from sight. But she saw Monsieur LeBer approaching his house.

How good he's been to me, she thought, welcoming me into his beautiful home—me, an enemy of the French people by the peculiar rules of warfare. And I have found myself *liking* these Papists. How can I help it? I would never have believed it possible a few short months ago!

Lydia walked over near the crucifix on the wall. Perhaps there will come a time, she thought, when I will understand how a woman like Mother Bourgeoys can enjoy a life of sacrifice and why a gentleman like Monsieur Meriel, who might have lived elegantly on inherited wealth is happy to devote his life to others.

As the Puritan girl turned away, she realized that she had to know more about this Papist religion. I wonder, she thought, if it is wrong of me to want to know more?

5.

The Miraculous Statue

The day finally arrived when Lydia was able to go downstairs. Dinner was served at midday, she learned, and she looked about excitedly as she descended the steep staircase. Madame Dupont had lent her a gold brooch to wear at her throat.

Lydia followed the housekeeper through the elegant hallway to the dining room, where Monsieur LeBer and a young man awaited her. This was her first glimpse of Pierre LeBer—the only son at home—

a young man of about twenty-five, she decided.

Lydia smiled as he was introduced to her. She thought him rather a dude, for he was dressed so differently from the young Puritan men of Groton. He wore buff-colored breeches, an embroidered waistcoat, blue coat, silk stockings, and buckled shoes. The cascade of lace at his throat was beautiful. His hair was powdered and tied in a *queue*. Pierre was quiet and well-mannered, and Lydia was sure she would like him.

She felt a little in awe of the well-appointed table covered with linen cloth, sparkling glassware, decanters of wine, and an abundance of delicious food served by a maid whom Monsieur LeBer called Thérèse. At Lydia's place was a napkin, plate, silver goblet, fork and spoon, and there was also a curious little sheath from which a knife protruded.

As she looked about, she thought of the table board and wooden dishes back home in the Longley kitchen, and a feeling of sadness pervaded her. That happy family life was gone. Monsieur LeBer's voice interrupted her thoughts.

"How are you feeling, my dear?" he asked as he filled her plate with roast chicken, peas, and potatoes, while Thérèse passed the cucumber salad.

"Very well, thank you, sir," Lydia answered in French.

She was gratified to see the smile of pleasure which swept his face.

"The sisters have taught you well, I see," he commented briefly.

During the meal Lydia asked Monsieur LeBer if she could help Madame Dupont about the house.

"I would be glad to work, sir, for I was always busy at home. I miss my duties."

"Madame Dupont will find something for you to do if you wish," answered Monsieur LeBer in French. "I'm sure you can dust and polish the silver and pewter for her at least."

He removed a leather case from his pocket and took out a knife which he used to cut the chicken. "Lydia, your knife is in that silken case," he explained. "Carry it with you when you think you will have need to use it, for the time will come when you will eat an occasional meal elsewhere, possibly at Madeleine de Maricourt's. She is my niece and I hope will be your friend. It is the custom here in New France for each person to carry his own knife wherever he goes."

"Everything seems so different to me, sir," answered Lydia simply. "I have much to thank you for."

She studied the beautifully decorated room—the deep red velvet hangings at the windows, the silver candlesticks, the ornate French clock on the mantel above the roaring flame which felt so comfortable. The late autumn was cold in Ville-Marie, and a fire had been built in each room.

She noticed the massive sideboard filled with silver and china, and her eyes were drawn to the fine oil paintings on the walls—imported from France, she decided.

What a beautiful home, Lydia thought, yet Monsieur LeBer is not a happy man. One can easily see that.

Pierre had been eating quickly and in silence. Lydia realized at once he was as shy and serious as she. Suddenly, however, he spoke to her.

"Would you like to take a stroll this afternoon? I'll be glad to show you around if you feel strong enough."

Lydia was delighted to be able to understand his rapid French.

"I'd love to go," she exclaimed, eyes shining.

How often lately, while watching people pass beneath her window, had she longed to go outside.

Soon she and Pierre were chatting like old friends. He told her how Monsieur Meriel had come to New France four years before to act as chaplain at the hospital and as spiritual director of the pupils and sisters at the Congregation de Notre Dame. He explained that priests must accept whatever assignments their superiors give them and go wherever sent, regardless of personal inclination.

"I found it very hard to get accustomed to his priestly garments," confided Lydia shyly. "But now I've become used to seeing his black cassock, as he calls it, his white rabat, and purple cuffs. He called on me several times during my illness. He explained that Sulpician priests dress differently from other orders of priests."

"That is true," replied Monsieur LeBer, "just as do the various orders of sisters. They, too, have outer distinguishing marks to tell one from another."

"How I admire Mother Bourgeoys!" exclaimed Lydia.

"We all do." Pierre's enthusiasm showed in his voice. "In the forty years she's spent here, she's shown marvelous courage and strength of character. She's suffered untold disappointments, and still she works faithfully among her pupils, teaching them love of God and of our Lady."

"Are you satisfied with the clothes the dressmaker is making for you?" Monsieur LeBer asked. "And the ones she has completed? Do you enjoy your new shoes with the red heels, too?" He smiled kindly at her as she nodded in quick response.

"Oh, Monsieur, I can never repay you for your kindness. I have a beautiful new coat, trimmed with luxurious fur. I've never owned clothes of such fine quality, nor so many! I like the pretty colors, too, though I feel a bit guilty wearing them. Pastor Hobart would surely disapprove of me."

Both Pierre and his father raised their eyebrows questioningly. "Pastor Hobart?" repeated the young man. "Who is he?"

"He was our minister in Groton, and a fine man, but very stern. I don't know what he'd say if he could see me in these elegant clothes."

"Don't worry about it," said Monsieur LeBer. "It gives me pleasure to see you in them. How I wish my own. . ." But he never finished the sentence. Pierre glanced quickly at him.

In the silence that followed, Lydia spoke again. "My best dress is to be black silk, and the cobbler is making me black shoes to go with it. I will wear those outside of the house because of the loss of my people. They will be more fitting." Lydia turned aside as she brushed the tears away. "But don't these things cost you a great deal, Monsieur? Can you afford to give me these luxurious clothes?"

"My child, don't bother your pretty head about the cost. I enjoy making others happy. My fur business has been very lucrative, and I only wish my dear wife were with me to enjoy a happy old age."

The three continued their meal in silence. As they rose to leave the table, Monsieur LeBer told Lydia that Pierre was an artist and that she must see some of his paintings.

"I'm planning to try one of Mother Bourgeoys," said Pierre. "She has an expressive face and I hope to catch her strength of character."

When the young man and woman left the house later, Lydia thought Pierre looked very handsome in his hat with the turned-up brim and scarlet silk lining, his ribbon-trimmed gloves, and long-tailed coat. She paused and looked back at the spacious home.

Pierre called her attention to the pointed roof and the fact that the first floor was even with the street. She saw that the house had little dormer windows with iron shutters, and that its walls were thick stone. She had observed the wooden beams inside and the odd iron hinges shaped like the letter "S."

As they walked along Rue St. Paul, she found that Pierre chatted quite comfortably with her. She couldn't understand all that he said, but she gathered he was talking about the good times enjoyed by the people of Ville-Marie during the winter months. Mountains of snow fell, he said, and it was fun to sleigh on the St. Lawrence River, which became a mammoth frozen highway for many miles.

As he talked, Lydia enjoyed looking about. There was an apothecary shop with windows full of glass bottles, and a fur shop displaying elegant beaver skins beautifully marked. Most interesting of all to Lydia was the cobbler shop of Monsieur St. Pierre. She could see the big red-faced man seated at his bench, his calloused hands drawing a huge needle through the sole of a man's leather shoe.

Many of the people they passed bowed and spoke respectfully to Pierre, who politely took off his hat to each. He explained to Lydia that some of these men were *habitants*, cultivators of the soil. She noticed that they wore long-skirted, dark grey frocks with attached hoods and matching trousers. Most of them wore either moccasins or boots. She decided they were the workmen of Ville-Marie. Some were smoking short little pipes and inquired for Monsieur LeBer and for the recluse.

Pierre presented one young woman as his cousin Paul's wife, Madeleine de Maricourt. Lydia could see that her hair was powdered and arranged in tight little curls which peeped out from under the brim of her hat. She wore a beautiful fur coat. Lydia liked her and was pleased to be invited to come to see her. Perhaps they'd be friends.

The wind was cold off the river and Lydia shivered and drew her coat collar more closely about her neck. Not far away the spires of a church dominated the countryside.

"That's Bonsecours," said Pierre, and Lydia was fascinated to see the church Mother Bourgeoys had built. She wondered what a Papist church looked like inside—if it resembled the meetinghouse back in Groton. She was glad when Pierre suggested they go in.

He stood politely aside, holding the door open for her, but when he saw how uncertain she was, he led the way, motioning her to follow.

A strange feeling came over Lydia. There was an atmosphere of silence and holiness inside the church. She saw several people kneeling, lips moving in prayer, eyes turned toward a wooden statue of Mary upon which rested a crown of diamonds. The miraculous statue!

Pierre walked straight down to the front of the church and knelt at the rail. Lydia knelt beside him, entranced by the beautiful altar where candles flickered in the slight breeze. She watched Pierre rise and light a single candle, then kneel once again.

"Help me to do what is right, dear Lord," she prayed. "Bless my dear family in heaven and take care of John and Monsieur LeBer." She turned to gaze at the strange wooden statue and a feeling of peace engulfed her.

As Lydia waited for Pierre to finish his prayers, she thought about the meetinghouse in Groton where she and Jemima had sat side by side so many weeks before. She could see in her mind's eye the large bare room completely devoid of religious objects, which she knew her father would call idol-

atrous, the gallery on three sides, the rough timbers
and crude benches. She knew the unattractive room
had held definite solace for many people, but she
sensed in this church a Something, a warm celestial
Presence, which she had never been aware of in the
meetinghouse. She couldn't explain it and her con-
science troubled her. Was she being disloyal to her
family and her Puritan faith? Lydia was glad when
Pierre rose and led the way outside.

"Why did you light the candle, Pierre?" she
asked as they walked briskly back in the direction
of Rue St. Joseph.

"I was saying a prayer for you, Lydia," he replied seriously and with no apparent self-conscious-
ness. "Some day I will tell you what I asked the
Blessed Mother to give you."

6.

THE FAITH OF VILLE-MARIE

One morning Lydia awakened very early as had been her custom at home. Someone was leaving the house. Lydia could barely distinguish the forms of two women walking off in the direction of Rue St. Paul. Just then the bells of Notre Dame, the parish church, sounded for Mass. Madame Dupont and Thérèse must be going to Mass at five instead of at half-past six as they usually did.

I wonder why these people attend a church service each day, Lydia pondered, as she crept back into bed. She shivered and wrapped the warm quilts more tightly about her shoulders, for the morning chill was penetrating. Wide awake now, she lay thinking about the LeBers and their household, and the influence of their faith upon their lives.

They call the service "Mass," she said to herself, and there's something about it that draws them. It certainly doesn't do them any harm and it must be a comfort to know that the church is open every day, not just on the Sabbath as was our meetinghouse. I wonder what a Mass is like.

At breakfast Lydia told Thérèse she had seen her going to early Mass.

"We didn't go to five o'clock Mass, Mademoiselle," replied the maid. "You must have seen Mademoiselle LeBer and Anne Barroy. They go out every morning at quarter to five."

Why, Lydia wondered, does Jeanne LeBer stay alone in her room? What is the purpose behind such a life?

One day Monsieur LeBer asked Lydia if she would like to attend Mass with him and Pierre each morning at seven.

For just a fraction of a moment Lydia hesitated. Monsieur LeBer has been good to me, she thought. I can at least repay him by attending his church. I'd love to go once, but every day! Yet, since it evidently means so much to him, it's the least I can do.

"I'd be glad to, sir," she answered.

"Monsieur Meriel celebrates seven o'clock Mass at the Hotel-Dieu chapel. You won't understand it at first, but I hope in time you'll grow to understand it and love it as we do. We will pray for you each day. Perhaps you will pray for us, *ma petite*. Ask God to grant me understanding of His will."

Lydia was a bit embarrassed to hear him ask for her prayers. Puritans were not in the habit of asking people to pray for them and it sounded strange to her. She realized, though, that her benefactor, this French Papist, possessed a genuine belief in prayer and faith in God's divine guidance. Religion was close to the daily life of this family.

The next morning in the chapel Monsieur LeBer knelt for a long time in prayer, his face sad in repose. Then he took a string of black beads from his pocket and his lips moved as he fingered them. I must ask Pierre what those beads are, thought Lydia, as she bowed her head in silent prayer.

As the Mass progressed, Lydia found it difficult
to know when to stand and when to kneel. But,
despite the fact that she understood no part of the
service, it appealed to her love of beauty. Candles
flickered on the altar. Monsieur Meriel, clad in rich
vestments, moved slowly about and Lydia enjoyed
watching him. Everyone seemed intent upon the
action at the altar.

The statues of Joseph and Mary and the figure of
Christ on the Cross were becoming familiar sights
to the English Puritan girl, for it seemed that every-
where one encountered replicas of Jesus' family in
New France—in the house, on the streets, in the
churches. Suddenly she realized for the first time
that her own life was under the protection of the
Holy Family. This thought filled her with peace
and she was glad she had come. She felt closer to
God than ever before.

Lydia was surprised that Mass was soon over.
How different it was from the Puritan service of
several hours! Outside the church several people
chatted merrily, and Monsieur LeBer introduced
Lydia to a number of his friends. Everyone was cor-
dial to the English girl and seemed pleased that she
spoke their language. She felt strangely at home in

this environment so different from the little town in New England which had always been her home. She liked the friendliness and gaiety of these people as they laughed and joked together. How much different from the solemnity and restraint of Puritans!

Later, as she sat in her room knitting before the fire, Lydia found herself thinking again of the Mass she had attended that morning—and of Jeanne LeBer.

She knew now that Monsieur LeBer's daughter was a most unusual person. Although Jeanne attended Mass each morning, Lydia had never seen her leave her room at the end of the hallway. No one seemed to visit Madamoiselle LeBer except Anne Barroy and Mother Bourgeoys and sometimes one of the priests. Anne Barroy arrived by dawn each morning and left the LeBer house early each afternoon.

Lydia's thoughts were interrupted by a knock on the door. "Monsieur Meriel is here to see you," Thérèse called.

I think I shall ask him about Jeanne LeBer, Lydia decided impulsively, as she pulled up a second chair by the fire.

Soon the friendly priest was seated opposite Lydia, rubbing his hands together to warm them.

"You're looking very well, Lydia," he observed. "Monsieur LeBer is taking good care of you." He smiled. "Do you miss New England terribly?"

Lydia's face sobered. "It's difficult for me to realize that my family is gone. It all seems like a nightmare—and I wonder if I'll ever awaken. Did Monsieur LeBer tell you he has heard that John is still with the Abenaki and is well and happy?"

"Yes, so he told me. Your brother evidently likes the outdoor life."

Lydia nodded. "The woods always beckoned him. Hunting and fishing were his favorite pastimes. I wish I might see him again," she added wistfully.

"Don't give up hope. Perhaps you will. Have you met anyone outside of the LeBer family?"

"Oh, yes. Pierre took me to see Madeleine de Maricourt."

"Good! Madeleine will see that you meet other young folks. You mustn't stay alone too much. This house isn't what it used to be when Madame LeBer was alive. It's sad and still. They tell me that Monsieur entertained a lot in those days, but now the heart of the home has departed. And since

Jeanne lives here in the house as a recluse, people are somewhat in awe. They don't feel free to come here the way they used to."

"I notice that they inquire for her, though," said Lydia. "I have been curious to hear about her for weeks. Will you tell me her story, *mon père?*"

"This is a fine opportunity to do just that," answered the priest. "We can talk uninterruptedly, and I'm sure Monsieur LeBer wishes you to know about her, although he can't bring himself to tell you. He is brokenhearted, for she is a beautiful girl and his only daughter. He finds it hard to reconcile himself to her sacrifice."

"Just what is a recluse, *mon père?*"

"A recluse is a person who lives withdrawn from the world."

"But why does a person decide to live like that?"

"That will take a little explaining, especially to you, Lydia, since you are not of our faith," answered the priest. He seemed to be pondering how best to clarify her thoughts on the matter. "You admire Mother Bourgeoys, don't you?" he asked.

Lydia nodded. "Of course."

"Mother Bourgeoys came over here to New France because she wished to teach children not only reading and writing, but religion—the truths of the Church. She has taken voluntary vows of chastity and poverty and has dedicated her life to this one purpose. Why do you suppose she has done this?"

Lydia hesitated. "Because she wanted to?"

"It was more than that, dear girl," the priest explained. "Mother Bourgeoys loved God so much that she wanted to prove it to Him by making a sacrifice of her life and working in His service. It is a common practice for Catholics to enjoy making sacrifices."

"How strange," said Lydia. "But it's a wonderful thing to do, just for love of God, isn't it?"

"We feel it is necessary for a certain number of people to be an example of goodness to others. There are those who feel they are called by God to live in this way. I felt I must leave behind me a life of wealth and ease to work for God. There is an immense personal satisfaction in helping the poor and the sick to find comfort and in teaching them how to appreciate their faith and lead good lives."

"But what has this to do with Jeanne LeBer?" asked Lydia.

"I am leading up to that," replied Monsieur Meriel. "Sacrifice is of many kinds and degrees. Catholics believe that sacrifice strengthens character. Our Lord sacrificed His life for the sins of the world, and we Catholics believe that suffering for His sake is exemplary and proves our love for the divine Savior.

"Mother Bourgeoys and I are examples of one kind of sacrifice, but a recluse like Jeanne LeBer practices another kind. We are out in the world among people, for we believe that we can help them more by mingling with them. But Jeanne feels that she can better show her love for God by living apart in seclusion, turning her back on the wealth that is hers, existing almost in squalor, having little intercourse with human beings. She attends Mass early each morning, meditates at intervals all day, knits and sews for the poor, and embroiders church linens and vestments.

"They tell me that when her father came here from Normandy in 1657 he was gay, robust, and fearless. He married Jeanne Le Moyne, sister of the man who was later to be his business associate. Their first child was Louis, now living in France. Their second, in 1662, was the lovely little girl whom they named Jeanne for her mother."

"Then she is thirty-two years old now," mused Lydia.

"She was beautiful, the pride of her father's heart. When she was eight, they sent her up to the Ursuline convent in Quebec for schooling. Her father's sister, Marie, was a nun there, and Jeanne was a model student. She showed a marked love for prayer and spirituality, even then, young as she was. But she was always friendly, gracious, and had intense pity for the poor.

"At fifteen she came home," continued Monsieur Meriel, "her education finished, and her father and mother were ever so proud of their charming daughter. By now there were other children—four boys. They hoped to introduce Jeanne to Montreal society. Monsieur LeBer had done well in the fur business. He is a self-made man, an exceptionally fine, honest person who has devoted his life to Ville-Marie, abided by it laws, and been a most generous benefactor of the Church."

"How good he has been to me," murmured Lydia.

"Jeanne LeBer has been called the richest girl in New France. She would bring to marriage a dowry of tremendous proportions. Monsieur LeBer and his wife enjoyed buying her beautiful clothes and hoped she would marry well. In fact, François Charron, who is associated with Monsieur LeBer in business, has always been devoted to Jeanne, but she was never interested in romance. They begged her to consider marriage, but she told them she had made a private promise not to marry."

The priest shook his head. "While she wore the silk gowns her mother provided for her, she hid underneath a haircloth shirt next to her tender skin. Although she charmingly graced the fine table where her father entertained men and women of dignity and importance, she preferred to visit the nuns at the Hotel-Dieu or the congregation and discuss spiritual matters. Although she attended parties, she left them and went outside to spend quarter-hours in prayer and meditation.

"To reach a state of greater perfection of spirit, she divided her days into hours for prayer, sewing, reading, and trying to get closer to the spirit of Christ. She longed to make a supreme sacrifice and unite herself with God, separated from the world, for she had long admired a saint named Catherine of Siena who had made a domestic retreat years before. Jeanne consulted her confessor, a Sulpician priest

like myself. He suggested she try a term of proba-
tion first, if her father were willing. He could see
that she was determined, and he felt that perhaps a
five-year trial might prove her wrong. He told
Jeanne he would consult his own superiors on the
matter."

"How strange all this seems," said Lydia, "and
what a terrible disappointment for her father and
mother."

"That is true," replied Monsieur Meriel, "but
perhaps Jeanne was *marked* for this life of sacrifice
to make reparation and to be an example to the
people of Ville-Marie. She took her first vow for
five years and tested herself from 1680 to 1685.
During that time her mother died. She had told her
parents that her chamber would become her cell,
and she didn't leave it even to attend her mother in
her dying moments, although she later paid respects
to her dead body. She believed she was right to act
as she did, although such action may seem strange
to us.

"When her temporary vow was ended, her father
naturally hoped she would resume family life and
help him bring up her four brothers. He was terribly disappointed when she renewed her vow for

five more years of solitude. God must surely be calling her, for again four years ago she took the third vow of reclusion which will be over next year."

"Poor Monsieur LeBer," sighed Lydia.

"Jeanne has a strong effect upon those who see her. They feel they are looking upon a living saint. I won't be surprised if she sends Anne Barroy to ask you to come to her chamber. She must be eager to meet you."

"Do you really think so?" gasped Lydia. "I'd like so much to see her. Then I might better understand why she has done this thing. I see now why Monsieur LeBer asked me to pray that he would be able to accept the will of God."

"It's strange that God directed you, a Puritan, to this house, Lydia, to be a second daughter to Monsieur LeBer." Monsieur Meriel paused for a moment and seemed to be reflecting on the strange fortunes of the LeBer family. "Jeanne LeBer is revered by the people of New France," he went on, "for making this supreme sacrifice and for renouncing the riches so rightfully hers. They feel that this girl's sacrifice may bring good fortune on their country."

"Will she always remain here in her father's house?"

"No. Plans are being made even now for her to enter the Congregation when the new chapel is completed. You have seen it in the making. Doubtless it will be finished by next summer. Jeanne LeBer gave Mother Bourgeoys a large part of the funds necessary to pay for it, but she made one stipulation."

"What was that?"

"That she be allowed to become a member of the community, occupy a cell directly behind the altar, and be called thereafter Sister LeBer. Mother Bourgeoys has consented, provided the ecclesiastical authorities agree. Jeanne's third vow of reclusion ends next year, and I'm quite certain she will then leave here forever."

Lydia sat in silence. What courage and love of God! She wondered if she would ever be able to make such a sacrifice for Him. I'd rather teach as Mother Bourgeoys and her sisters do, she decided.

"Monsieur Meriel, what is Anne Barroy's part in this?"

"Anne Barroy is Monsieur LeBer's niece, Lydia. She is a humble, modest girl who wishes to attend to Jeanne's personal needs. For many years a maidservant waited on her, but now Anne Barroy comes in daily, does her simple washing, takes her tray of food to her, accompanies her to Mass at a quarter to five each morning, and builds her fire. She is considering entering the convent herself as a teaching sister."

Monsieur Meriel talked for a while longer and then left Lydia to look back on a day in which she had learned so much about the religious practices of the LeBers, the sacrifice of Jeanne, and the faith of Ville-Marie.

7.

The Summons and the Meeting

One midwinter afternoon Lydia heard the merry jingling of sleigh bells outside, the stamp of feet, and the gay voice of Madeleine de Maricourt at the door.

"Bundle up in your warmest clothes, Lydia," she commanded, laughing. "You're coming with me for a ride in the carriole. The river is frozen solid."

Lydia was thrilled, but a bit cautious, too, for she had never done such a thing. "Do you have a driver?" she asked.

"Of course not." Madeleine laughed at Lydia's timidity. "I have Old Tim, a horse we've driven for years. Hurry now, for it gets dark early."

Lydia put on a thick beaver coat and woolen scarf. Winter temperatures in Ville-Marie were always below freezing. Soon the girls were speeding smoothly along in the direction of the St. Lawrence, a red homespun blanket wrapped about them.

"We'll ride a while and then stop at Longueuil, my husband's family home. His father died some years ago, and his brother, Charles, lives there now."

Madame Dupont had told Lydia about the family of Madeleine's husband, the Le Moynes. "They represent the best of the French people," she had said.

"They are one of the most distinguished families in New France. When Charles Le Moyne, Paul's father, came to Ville-Marie as a boy, he learned some of the Indian dialects and became indispensable to the early settlers in dealing with the Indians. When Monsieur Le Moyne was twenty-one, King Louis XIV granted him a tract of land across the St. Lawrence from Ville-Marie. The king bestowed on him the title of seigneur, and the young seigneur called his estate, or seigneury, Longueuil."

Lydia learned that Monsieur LeBer, too, had received the title of seigneur as an honor from the king for his good work in dealing with the Iroquois, and that all the seigneurs received free grants of land. They were obliged, however, to clear a certain amount of it each year. They gathered together *habitants* to live on it and cultivate it. The *habitants* paid the seigneurs a tiny rent of produce and a nominal fee once a year on St. Martin's Day. They lived comfortably, but they had to work six days a year without pay on the seigneur's land, and they were obliged to fight for him in time of war. This feudal system seemed to work to the contentment of both seigneurs and *habitants*.

"Monsieur Le Ber entered the fur trade with Charles Le Moyne," Madame Dupont had explained, "and married his sister. Both the Le Moynes and the LeBers lived for many years on this very street as neighbors, even though Seigneur Le Moyne had been granted such a large amount of land across the river. There were two daughters and eleven sons in the Le Moyne family. Paul, Madeleine's husband, is an officer in the marines. Charles, another son, has established a beautiful manor house at Longueuil."

This was the home to which Madeleine was taking her young friend. They skimmed along the river, their sleigh bells jingling in tune with the bells of other sleighs. French songs rang out in the frosty air.

Madeleine looked across at lovely, rosy-cheeked Lydia. Impulsively she said, "Lydia, I've never known anyone like you. To tell the truth, I really never knew an English girl before, except for some of the English captives in the service of French families here in Ville-Marie or in the seigneuries beyond. You are the first one I've known well, simply because you're living in my uncle's house. All of my other friends are French—and Catholic, too."

"Am I so different from them?" Lydia looked dismayed.

"Yes, in a way you are. You're more serious. You don't laugh so much—and you're not so fond of clothes as we are. And you're *ever* so pretty!"

Lydia laughed. "Well, truthfully," she said, "I sometimes feel guilty wearing such lovely dresses and gay shoes. What few clothes I had in Groton were very drab. We were forbidden to wear bright colors. Pastor Hobart would have chided my parents if I had dared to wear such a bright blue dress as I have on right now. And this vivid blanket in plain sight of everyone!"

As Madeleine pulled on the reins to slow the speeding horse, her face grew serious. "Do you think of Groton often—and of the terrible thing that happened to your people?"

"I shall never get over it," Lydia replied sadly. "It comes back to me at night especially, and whenever I catch a glimpse of Indians on the streets. I can't believe that my family could have met so terrible a death—and that I escaped."

"I'm so glad Uncle Jacques found you at the intendant's office and took you home with him. He's very fond of you, and it's good for him and Pierre to have a young girl about. Jeanne's decision has made life hard for them. Yet she is adored by the people of Ville-Marie and of all New France. In time, her sacrifice may accomplish great things for this country. It may be the means of obtaining the grace of reform for some of our people."

"I have been hoping to meet her. Is she very beautiful?"

"She was lovely in her teens. I remember the day she came home from the Ursuline convent in

Quebec. I'll tell you about it over a cup of hot chocolate. Look, you can see part of Longueuil over
there—the stables and sheds clustered nearby, and
the stone mill." As they came nearer, Lydia watched
closely. The manor house was a long, low stone
building with overhanging gables and a peaked roof.

A smiling housekeeper met the girls at the door.
Madeleine led the way into the comfortable salon,
suggesting refreshments in front of the blazing fireplace.

"Where is my brother-in-law and the rest of the
family?" she asked, after she had greeted the
woman.

"There is no one here, Madame. They are all out
coasting. But I will bring you some chocolate and
sweet pasties."

As the girls warmed their freezing fingers over
the flames, they continued their discussion of
Jeanne LeBer.

"She was only fifteen when her father went by
boat the 180 miles to Quebec to fetch her home. For
weeks before, he and his wife had been anticipating
the great event. Their only daughter was finally
coming home to stay! The nuns had trained her
beautifully, as only they can, and her manners were

charming. She could sew and embroider and was well-versed in religion, reading, and writing.

"Her parents had redecorated her room. There were silken draperies at the windows. A sumptuous bed had arrived from France. The closet was filled with exquisite clothes—even a set of pure white furs. Truly it was an enchanting room!

"Because I was a special friend, I went over to stay with Madame LeBer and was there when Jeanne arrived. What rejoicing as she came up the street! Even the maids rushed out of the door to welcome her. I thought she was taller and slimmer than when I had last seen her. She seemed more thoughtful and dignified. Her big eyes were alight with happiness and she was so sweet to everyone. Monsieur LeBer couldn't take his proud eyes from her.

"But luxury never appealed to Jeanne. The joy of her parents in having her with them was short-lived as they watched her becoming more and more attached to reclusion. She is pale and thin, now, I hear, because she eats so little and is indoors so much. Her room is a veritable cell. I often wonder what made her do this thing. I couldn't—nor could I enter the convent, either. Could you, Lydia—that is, if you were a Catholic?"

"I don't know, Madeleine. They tell me one is called to the religious life. I wouldn't wish to live in solitude as she does, for I like people too well. But I do believe I'd enjoy teaching, like the sisters at the Congregation. I admire learning so much and have always longed to go to school myself."

"Wouldn't you rather be married, Lydia? Did you have a sweetheart in New England?"

Lydia shook her head slowly. "It's odd, I know, for most of the girls my age were married, just as they are here."

"What do you think of Pierre?" Madeleine persisted. "He's a very eligible bachelor, you know, one of the richest in Ville-Marie."

"Pierre is a fine young man, Madeleine. He's been most gallant in taking me to parties and introducing me to his friends. But he, too, is serious-minded and not particularly interested in young ladies. I wouldn't be surprised if he entered a religious order, would you?"

"We've all been expecting it for years, Lydia. Pierre's friend, François Charron, who was so fond of Jeanne, may join him when he takes the step. Perhaps he plans to stay at home with his father for the time being, or maybe he's looking about and biding his time to be absolutely certain of his vocation." Madeleine poured more chocolate from the silver pot.

"I wonder how you truly recognize a vocation." Lydia was so serious that Madeleine turned quickly to look at her. "Perhaps a voice inside whispers that you must serve God, that it's your destiny."

"Lydia," Madeleine asked suddenly, "do you ever have an inclination to become a Catholic?"

Lydia walked to the window and looked out for a moment at the piles of snow. Then she turned slowly.

"I often feel lonely, Madeleine, even though everyone is so generous and kind. Every so often I realize with a start that I'm all alone in the world—really alone—despite the fact that John still lives. Do you know what I do then? I walk over to Bonsecours Church where Pierre took me for the first time last October."

"I'm glad he took you there. All of us love Bonsecours."

"The doors are always open," Lydia continued, "and I go in—me, a Puritan from New England. Isn't it strange? I kneel before the miraculous statue and pour out my heart to God and to the Mother of

God. Her eyes seem to look down upon me so
understandingly. Sometimes I light a candle. After
a while, I'm refreshed. I have courage and I stop
worrying about the future.

"At first I felt guilty because I knew my father
and mother would never have been able to understand my turning to the Roman Church. But then I
told myself, Why shouldn't they be horrified?
They were never in a situation like mine. They
never met a Papist, so far as I know, nor saw a Catholic church. They couldn't understand. Perhaps, if
they're looking down on me, they will know that I
am trying to do what is right." Tears shone in the
girl's eyes.

Madeleine leaned over to pat Lydia's arm. "Of
course they will. Now we'd better be on our way,
my dear. It's getting dark."

As they climbed into the sleigh again and
skimmed along the St. Lawrence, they found the
river all but deserted. The laughing, caroling groups
had been scattered home by the swift winter darkness.

"I know Monsieur LeBer and Monsieur Meriel
are hoping I will find my way into the Church,
Madeleine." Lydia's thoughts had never left the

subject of faith. "More than anything else in the world I wish to please Monsieur LeBer. Other English captives are working, in service, for French families, but Monsieur LeBer is treating me as he would his daughter."

"Faith is a gift, Lydia. Perhaps someday God will give you that gift."

"I have asked Monsieur Meriel to lend me books, for I miss our family reading of the Bible each evening. Now that I can read French more easily, he has given me a prayer book and a volume of lives of the saints. These fine men and women must have loved the Church very much to have given their lives teaching others about it. Monsieur LeBer told me about priests who brave the wilderness to instruct the Indians. They learn Indian dialects and live in filth and poverty in order to Christianize the savages. That is the strongest proof I know that the Catholic Church has a divine mission."

"You're intelligent, Lydia, and good. You have much to bring to the Church. I believe that some day you'll love our faith and have the grace to accept it."

"All of you are so good to me."

"Tell me, Lydia," asked Madeleine, "was your

life in Groton so different from what it is here in Ville-Marie?"

"Oh, yes, Madeleine. We lived a simple country life on a small farm. Our lives were somewhat like those of the *habitants*, except that we owned our land."

Lydia thought of the social activity of the upper-class circle to which Madeleine and the LeBer family belonged. She pictured the seigneur's dinner table when he entertained Church dignitaries and government officials, the exquisite dresses worn by the women at formal parties, and the elegant clothing of the men in the height of fashion which had reached the French colony from the court of King Louis XIV.

"Puritan life in New England is somber, Madeleine," Lydia said at last. "There is no recreation to speak of. Dancing is forbidden, and our meeting-house is plain and bare, so different from the magnificence of many of your churches. In all my life I've never seen such beauty as midnight Mass on Christmas Eve."

"Have you thought that you might be sent back in an exchange of prisoners? Do you long to return to Groton?"

Lydia shook her head. "There's nothing left in Groton for me. It would be sad to go back and, besides, I don't know if I would fit there any more. I do know that I can't live indefinitely in your uncle's house. I wouldn't feel free to do so and I'll probably never marry. I do wonder if there isn't something I can do here in Ville-Marie to be of use."

"Uncle Jacques will never let you leave his home, Lydia, unless you wish to. You are his ward, you know, and in many ways you are taking the place of Jeanne. I'll pray that you have peace of mind."

Madeleine never dreamed that the very next morning her friend would find a great measure of peace. When Lydia opened her bedroom door to a gentle knock, Anne Barroy stood before her.

"Jeanne LeBer wishes to meet you. Are you free to come now?"

Lydia followed Anne to the last mysterious doorway at the end of the corridor. For a moment she paused on the threshold of the room which her guide motioned her to enter. She looked through the open door into a chamber unbelievably bare and bleak. Here was none of the elegance and opulence of the rest of the LeBer home. Furnishings included only the simplest necessities for physical existence and spiritual meditation. The bed was a mere pallet of straw, partly covered by a shabby coverlet of homespun. There were a chest of drawers, a table, a spinning wheel, a chair or two. A small iron stove barely took the chill from the air. Lydia saw a few books on a shelf, a prie-dieu in one corner, religious pictures on the wall, a statue of the Blessed Mother. There were no curtains, no carpets, no looking glass.

It seemed to Lydia that she had been standing there in the doorway for hours. Actually it was only a split second before her attention centered on the frail young woman bending over the beautiful vestment she had been embroidering. As she looked up to greet her guest, Lydia gasped. She found herself staring at a face of rare spiritual beauty. Its pale fragility and unearthliness transformed it into that of a girl rather than of a woman over thirty.

As Jeanne LeBer rose to speak to Lydia in a sweet low voice, the vestment on which she had been working fell to her feet in folds. She was dressed in a long, drab woolen gown belted about her tiny waist.

She has a look of suffering, thought the Puritan girl, yet she is calm and resigned and . . . saint-like.

The magnetic charm of this consecrated woman so filled the chamber that Lydia soon forgot the cell-like surroundings as Jeanne drew from her the tragic story of her family and of her long journey to New France with the savages. Anne Barroy had left the room, and the two sat facing each other as they talked. The girl from Groton, usually reserved, poured out her story with such ease and openness that she was amazed later when she recalled her visit with Jeanne LeBer.

"My dear child, there is meaning in all that has happened," said Jeanne softly when Lydia had finished. "God has sent you here for a purpose. You have unusual courage and an uncommon depth of character. And you have brought a measure of comfort to my beloved father which has helped to ease the pain of separation which he feels I have caused him. There must surely come a time when you will understand why this thing has happened to you and to your family."

"Will I ever become reconciled to the loss of my dear ones?" asked Lydia, sadly shaking her head. "*Resigned* I must be—and ever grateful to your father for his humanity and generosity. But *reconciled* . . . ?"

"You will meet your loved ones again," continued Jeanne LeBer. "What comfort that thought alone can bring you! Each day you can pray for them as I shall pray for them and for you, too. I am so happy in my life—closer and closer to God." She looked about her. The wretched room no longer seemed bare and cold. "And when the new chapel for the Congregation is completed, I hope to live even nearer to Him, behind the altar next to the Blessed Sacrament."

Her liquid eyes glowed with shining resolve, and the fire of her faith seemed to envelop Lydia. "May you, too, find comfort and solace in our Holy Mother Church. Give of yourself unhesitatingly to God, Lydia, and you will be rewarded. I shall pray for the day to come quickly when you will approach the sacraments in all your love, and devotion, and understanding—and find true happiness."

As they rose, Jeanne lifted a corner of the brilliant vestment upon which she had been working.

"I will have this finished soon, and I trust it will be worn for many years in the new church. Do you think it beautiful?"

"The most exquisite thing I have ever seen," murmured Lydia.

"Nothing is too perfect for use in God's service." The hand Jeanne extended in farewell was thin and white, and the blue veins were prominent. It felt cold in Lydia's warm, capable grasp. Yet its clasp was firm.

Suddenly Mademoiselle LeBer turned to her bookshelf. "Here are my three beloved companions —the Psalter of David, *The Lives of the Saints*, and the Holy Bible."

"You have a Bible!" exclaimed Lydia. "How I have missed reading the familiar words! Every night we sat around the table at home while we took turns reading a chapter."

"My dear, let my father know your wish. He will find a Bible for you to have."

Jeanne walked with Lydia to the door. "I shall think of you often and pray for you. You have brought comfort to this house. We may never talk again—I do not know—for I have taken vows, but we shall meet in heaven."

As Lydia turned toward her own room, she felt as if she had, in some way, brushed against an angel and that the prayers of Jeanne LeBer could not but help bring her blessings.

8.

LYDIA'S FAMILY

Ville-Marie, in the year 1695, was an exciting spot. History was in the making, and Lydia Longley, as a member of the LeBer household, found herself in the very center of it. Intelligent, sensitive, and affectionate, she felt keenly anything which affected the family of the man who had befriended her. And more and more she felt herself drawn toward the warm faith which the family

professed and which affected all of them more
deeply than anything else.

Lydia later traced her growing faith to that Feb-
ruary night when she was awakened by loud pounding on her door. She could never forget her fear as
Pierre shouted, "Fire! Fire! Get up, Lydia. The
Hotel-Dieu chapel is burning."

She awoke to see her room glowing with light.
Outside, the narrow street was filled with people. In
the glare Lydia could see shadowy figures vainly
trying to fight the roaring flames of the building so
close to the LeBer house. She flung on her clothes,
snatched her coat, and fled down the stairs to be met
by blazing heat and choking fumes.

Priests, nuns, and lay people had joined forces to
fight the enemy which had already caused so many
tragic losses for the people of Ville-Marie. There
was little they could do amid mountains of snow and
ice in the cruel midwinter night. Everything was
frozen.

All night long Lydia helped the sisters with the
sick, taking some of them into the house, making
them comfortable, serving them hot coffee. The
relentless blaze burned the chapel to the ground and
destroyed much of the hospital. The fire had pro-

gressed so far before it was discovered that nothing had been saved from the church and little from the hospital.

In the chill winter's dawn the exhausted Hospitaller Sisters surveyed the ruins with tear-filled eyes. The results of their labors lay before them in ashes.

"God will help us rebuild our hospital," said a small, lovely featured sister. Her eyes were sad, but in her face was a look of strength. "We must pray for perseverance. Our beloved foundress, Sister Jeanne Mance, faced misfortunes, too. We cannot fail her now."

What trust in God! thought Lydia. And her own faith and trust seemed to begin then to take root.

Pierre and his friend, François Charron, had just carried a patient into the LeBer home. As they came out, Pierre walked over to Lydia. Rubbing his cold hands together, he said, "We'll miss daily Mass in the chapel, won't we, Lydia?" He sighed. "Poor Sister Jeanne Mance. For many years she has lain buried there, and now her body is destroyed by the flames of this miserable night. But the spirit of the Angel of the Colony will never die."

Lydia turned to look at his face, pinched and blue under the beaver cap. "You must have something hot to drink—some coffee, Pierre. You're tired and freezing. Come in for a few minutes. It's bitter out here."

Pierre looked up at the sky. "Father has been watching the wind all night. A shift in direction and this house, too, would be flat on the ground."

In the hallway they found Madame Dupont and Thérèse serving coffee to weary fire-fighters and patients. Temporary beds had been set up in the salon and dining room.

Lydia heard one of the sick women say, "I suppose the recluse is on her knees upstairs. She must pray harder than ever after this night of ruin and misfortune."

No, Lydia would never forget that night. She had seen faith in action. The sisters of the Hotel-Dieu began, with God's help, the long task of rebuilding.

As spring neared, the great St. Lawrence River, vast sleighing and skating highway, began to run free again. The ice broke, and the boats, returning from the Old World, brought needed provisions as well as news from the court of King Louis XIV.

Fur trade with the Indians was booming. Monsieur LeBer and Pierre taught Lydia much about the fur business. She learned how dangerous it was for Frenchmen to go off into the wilderness to Indian settlements in search of skins. Monsieur LeBer explained the government's policy of encouraging the savages to bring furs to Ville-Marie. The city had established an annual King's Fair for that very purpose. It was held in June on the banks of the St. Lawrence River.

"This protects the lives of our family men, many of whom are being killed each year in the forests. And, by placing trade under the authority of the government, the fair protects the fur trade from unscrupulous and unlicensed merchants."

"What do you mean, sir?" asked Lydia.

"Some of our young men tire of the discipline and restrictions of Church and government. They paint themselves like Indians and roam the woods in unrestrained lawlessness. We call them *coureurs de bois*. Some form bands and stay away from home for several years, leaving needy wives and families unsupported. They carry on trade without licenses, give the Indians forbidden firewater, and, when they return to our colony, swagger about and spend their money on drunken debauches. Laws have been made to punish them, but they are difficult to enforce."

As the time approached for the King's Fur Fair, Lydia began to feel anxious at the thought of hundreds of savages arriving at the settlement. She knew that at the sight of them she could not help but relive the horrors she and her family had suffered at the hands of Indians only a year before. She wondered if she would hear from her brother John. There was a slight chance he might be brought to Ville-Marie. She decided to ask Pierre to make inquiries about the boy, for she had made up her mind to remain indoors during the ten-day fair.

"You mustn't do that," said Pierre when she told him. "I can understand your tragic memories and your intense fear of the Indians, but this is an annual event in Ville-Marie. You'll have to get used to it sometime. You must think it through, Lydia. The Iroquois are friendly to you English people and the Abenaki to us. My brother was killed by Indians only a few short years ago, but father and I have to face the fact that even savages differ as individuals.

These tragedies are the natural results of war, my dear, and we must accept them."

Lydia shivered and turned away, but Pierre persisted. "I want you to see the sights. Everyone gets dressed up as if for a carnival, and for three days the bargaining goes on. It's interesting to see. After that, I will admit the Indians get to drinking firewater with their boon companions, the *coureurs de bois*, and respectable people shut themselves up in their houses, locking doors and windows. I shall pity you then, for the screeching and shouting of the red men is horrible to hear. They run about, drunk and almost naked, brandishing their tomahawks. The authorities lose all control of them, and everyone is relieved when they finally leave town."

"It sounds dreadful," murmured Lydia. "I shall be glad when it's over."

For the next few days the entire settlement was astir. Merchants from all over New France came to Ville-Marie to set up temporary booths in which to display their wares. There was a contagious holiday atmosphere, and Lydia could not help being interested.

One morning she looked out of her window at an amazing sight. As far as she could see up the St.

Lawrence River were canoes—hundreds of them, a huge flotilla—filled with Indians coming down from the lakes. Some were kneeling, some standing, as they paddled their craft.

She ran down the stairs to meet Pierre coming in from outside.

"They're here, they're here," she said quickly.

"That's what I came back to tell you, Lydia. Come on. We'll watch them from the banking."

As they stood by the river, Pierre explained. "See where they're landing up there beyond the settlement?" He pointed to a distant spot. "The civil authorities have assigned them that area just out of town where they'll make camp for the night. They'll pull their canoes along the shore in a straight line, unload their beaver skins and kettles, and put up their wigwams. Tonight, from the house, you'll see their campfires against the sky. It's quite a sight."

"I had no idea there would be so many," murmured Lydia. "How can there possibly be a chance of finding John?"

"I'm going up to their encampment this afternoon with François Charron," said Pierre. "I'll try to find out something about your brother. Then tomorrow, when they come into Ville-Marie, we'll look for him—you and I."

Lydia glanced gratefully in his direction. "I pray he will be here."

At supper that night Pierre had no sure news. He and François had searched for a white boy called John Augary; they had found no one by that name. Lydia was dreadfully disappointed. For several hours she knelt at her window, watching the glowing flames from the Indian camp, praying that John was safe and happy.

The next morning Pierre and his father left the house early. Pierre promised to return for Lydia before the opening speeches, and she was ready for him. They moved through the throngs of people in the streets. Lydia had never seen so many human beings together at one time.

They squeezed into an empty spot where they could see the governor seated in his armchair in the middle of the city square. He wore his colorful official clothing, including a plumed hat and a sword which he held across his knees. Indians, ranged according to tribe, stood in a vast circle around him. Almost all of them were smoking pipes.

Painted and feathered, they carried bows and arrows, war clubs, or guns.

There were speeches of welcome. Pierre told Lydia no trading would be done until these customary ceremonies were completed. But soon it was over and the crowd dispersed.

The costumes of the people were a study in contrasts: *habitants* in their coarse grey clothes; gentlemen in fancy blue coats over embroidered waistcoats, silk stockings and buckled shoes, long curls falling to their shoulders; ladies in silks and laces, with beauty patches of plaster on their cheeks and curled, powdered hair; Sulpician priests, in their black robes with purple cuffs, strolling along with solemn faces; *coureurs de bois* painted garishly like the Indians; and finally the half-naked savages with glinting eyes, their bronze skins shining with grease and oil, their feathers quivering. Lydia kept close to Pierre and shrank back in terror whenever they passed too close to the red men.

They walked down by the river and watched the slow, deliberate manner of the Indians as they bargained for wares in exchange for beautiful beaver skins. Even by the palisade there were stalls.

For three days Lydia and Pierre covered miles,

it seemed, searching faces in the crowds, hoping to find John. It was of no use. He was nowhere about. Then they met a friendly Abenaki who told Pierre that he had seen John Augary, the paleface who had been living with Black Eagle. He was now in Acadia near the Penobscot River, many miles from Ville-Marie.

"At least he's still alive, Lydia," said Pierre as they turned toward home. "You may yet see him sometime. Don't give up hope."

The rest of the ten-day fair was a nightmare to Lydia, especially at night. She shivered with fear behind locked doors in the house on Rue St. Joseph. When the Indians finally left Ville-Marie, Monsieur LeBer was pleased with the results of his own trading and felt that the fur fair had been highly successful. But the memory of the disturbing affair stayed in Lydia's mind for many months.

Spring and summer brought completion of the new chapel for the sisters of the congregation and an undercurrent of tension in the LeBer household. The time for Jeanne to leave was drawing near. To enter the uncloistered congregation as a recluse was not a simple matter. Many legal and religious issues had to be clarified and agreed upon by all parties concerned. There were financial matters to be settled, too, for Jeanne was a wealthy woman.

Bishop Saint-Vallier, the successor of old Bishop Laval, was in France. Monsieur Dollier de Casson, superior of the Sulpician seminary and vicar-general of the diocese, was acting in place of the bishop. He felt it was fitting, in accordance with the ancient discipline of the Church, to give public solemnity to the occasion of Jeanne LeBer's entry into the congregation.

Lydia met the vicar-general in the hallway of the LeBer home one day. He was the tallest man she had ever seen, the picture of strength and kindness. Pierre had told her that the vicar-general had been a captain in the French cavalry and had become a priest because he detested the cruelties of war. He smiled at Lydia as he and several priests made their way upstairs to the recluse's chamber.

This was the day of the canonical examination. The priests would question Jeanne's motives for wishing to live as a recluse. It was a grave moment when the vicar-general later told Monsieur LeBer that "every previous assurance of her divine call to the extraordinary manner of life she is embracing, and of her determination to persevere in it until death, is reassured."

After hours of discussion among Monsieur LeBer, Pierre, Church authorities, and Mother Bourgeoys, a legal document was drawn up by which it was agreed that Jeanne should become a recluse in the Congregation de Notre Dame.

Jeanne's permanent reclusion was to begin on August 5, feast of Our Lady of the Snows. Plans for a solemn, but elaborate, ceremony were under way. Excitement ran high in Ville-Marie and in all New France, for Mademoiselle LeBer's heroism made a strong appeal to the public.

As for Lydia, she never climbed the stairs to her own room that she wasn't aware of the solitary figure behind closed doors at the end of the corridor.

One day Mother Bourgeoys told her about Jeanne's living quarters in the chapel, for Lydia wasn't to see the interior of the new church until the day of the ceremony. The cell was in reality three rooms, one above the other, at the back of the building. The basement room of the cell was in the sacristy. A grilled door would make it possible for Sister LeBer to look upon the altar and hear Holy Mass. Through the grille she would whisper her confession to the priest and receive Holy Communion. She would be handed her tray of meager food through a little window.

The room above was to be her sleeping chamber. Here her narrow bed would rest against the wall directly behind the high altar. Her pillow would be only a few inches from the Blessed Sacrament on the other side of the partition.

Above this was the workroom where Jeanne would sit to embroider materials for churches all over New France and to knit socks for the poor. There was an iron stove to provide a bit of heat during the cold winter months.

Jeanne's father and uncle had donated a beautiful silver sanctuary lamp. Pierre had furnished the stove for the church, and Jeanne herself had provided all the receptacles for the altar: monstrance, several vases, ciborium, chalice, and censer—things of beauty for her Savior.

On August 4 the legal contract was signed by all concerned at the Congregation, by the notary, and by the representative of the king. This document contained every possible stipulation for Jeanne LeBer's future life of solitude. Provision was even made that Anne Barroy should care for her personal needs.

Despite Lydia's excitement and anticipation, she worried constantly about Jeanne's father. Would he be able to endure the ceremony, knowing that he was parting from his only daughter? He was sixty-four years old, and, during the past few months, he had aged visibly. He presented a courageous front to the many friends who watched him sympathetically, but Lydia was relieved for his sake when August 5 finally arrived.

9.

The Sacrifice

It was late afternoon on August 5, feast of Our Lady of the Snows, the day Jeanne LeBer was to leave home forever. Lydia stood in front of the looking glass in her room before going downstairs to join the others.

Several months before, Monsieur LeBer had given her a bolt of white silk imported from France. "Jeanne's departure will be a solemn occasion, my dear," he had said sadly. "I want you to have a beautiful gown made from this white silk. You must be dressed properly."

The dressmaker had fashioned the gown with painstaking detail, adding touches of fine lace and sheer embroidery. With it Lydia wore a cap of handmade lace, dainty white slippers, and long white gloves. She looked lovely, her cheeks flushed and her hair curling in ringlets. She carried a silver rosary, a souvenir from Monsieur LeBer, and a leather-bound prayer book which Pierre had given her.

Lydia knelt to say a prayer for the saintly young woman, the heartbroken father, the kindly brother. "Please, God, give them the strength and courage to endure the sorrow of the next few hours."

Just outside the door she met the seigneur. Pale and drawn, he was on his way to his daughter's room for a final farewell before they went down to join the procession. He turned to Lydia for a moment and quietly clasped her hand.

"Courage, Monsieur," she whispered.

Downstairs Pierre stood in the open outer doorway. Lydia waited in the background. She was to walk beside him just behind his father and sister.

She would have felt strange and out of place in the intimate family circle but for the words of her guardian the day before.

"You are my ward, my dear. Your place is with us."

Suddenly Lydia heard the rhythmic sound of chanting in the distance. Pierre ran upstairs to tell his father that the officials were coming.

The sound of voices grew louder as the solemn procession moved down the narrow street. Monsieur Dollier de Casson led the way, followed by his clergy in magnificent robes. The crucifix was held high as they marched slowly past the house and then turned to retrace their steps.

Never had Lydia seen such an impressive group. There were relatives and close friends of the LeBer family and a number of men in military uniform. Then came high dignitaries of the colony and representatives of the court of France in curled wigs, elaborate costumes, lace collars and cuffs. Ladies were richly gowned in sumptuous silks and satins, their curls peeping out from under white caps. Many of them carried rosaries in gloved hands as they walked with eyes downcast.

Lydia watched the sisters of the Congregation

and of the Hotel-Dieu, their simple black habits such a contrast to the luxurious costumes of the other women. Behind them marched the girls of Ville-Marie, pupils at the convent, in white dresses and snowy linen caps or veils, their pure young faces glowing.

Colonists crowded into the street from Rue St. Paul, curious to catch a glimpse of the recluse as she left the house. Lydia recognized here and there the faces of poor people who had benefited from Monsieur LeBer's Christian generosity. Perhaps they were marveling at the life of ease and comfort which Jeanne LeBer was abandoning.

Then Lydia forgot everyone except the recluse, leaning on the arm of her white-haired father, who was walking slowly to their position behind the clergy. Her face was radiant, her step firm. She wore a long gown of grey serge encircled by a black leather belt. Her hair was concealed under a white linen covering which fell to her shoulders and formed a sort of kerchief coming to a point on her bosom. As she walked, her beautiful eyes were downcast, but for one moment she turned upon Lydia a look of affection and warmth.

As the procession moved toward the new chapel,

sacred hymns filled the air. Lydia watched the two people in front of her, and as they neared the entrance of the church she was shocked to see Monsieur LeBer leave his daughter's side, sobbing bitterly. She knew he hadn't the strength to face the final sacrifice of his own flesh and blood, that his heart was truly broken. She longed to run after him and offer words of consolation, but that she could not do.

Jeanne continued to move forward, following the priests into the church and down the aisle. She prostrated herself before the altar. Lydia and Pierre took seats at the front, along with the government officials, relatives, the sisters, and their pupils. The rest sat wherever they could find places, thus filling the entire chapel.

Monsieur Dollier de Casson presided over the ceremony. He blessed the cell behind the altar and then addressed a brief exhortation to the young woman, counseling her to persevere in her decision to live a consecrated solitary life as had Magdalen in her grotto. Then he escorted her within while the choir sang the litany of the Blessed Virgin. All eyes were on Jeanne's happy face as she left them for the rest of her life.

Lydia wept openly as she thought of the enormity of this sacrifice. God had two victims, really, she reflected—the girl and the father.

After the service Lydia and Pierre walked back to Rue St. Joseph, anxious because Monsieur LeBer would be alone in the empty house. As Lydia withdrew to her room, she heard Pierre knocking on the door of his father's chamber. There was a murmur of voices and then silence.

At supper Pierre announced that his father would not join them but would have a tray in his room.

"He's better off alone fighting the battle with himself. He'll be all right tomorrow. He has strength, Lydia, and deep religious devotion."

"The house feels strange and empty without her," said Lydia slowly. "I often thought of her as I walked about or sat in my room."

Pierre nodded. "We shall miss her, it is true, but I think God has marked her always for this life she has chosen. She will be happy."

Pierre sat back in his chair and seemed, for a few moments, to be far away from the dining room on Rue St. Joseph. Finally he spoke. "I came to a decision today, Lydia—something that I have long been considering."

Lydia looked up quickly.

"I want to serve the Church, too. But I want to do something different from the Sulpicians or the Jesuits. I should like to found an order of men who would serve the sick in hospitals—like the sisters at the Hotel-Dieu. We would call ourselves Frères Hospitallers."

"How wonderful!" Lydia's eyes were shining. "There's great need for male nurses among the poor and sick of the colony."

"François Charron is interested, too. We're hoping to get permission from the religious authorities to establish such an institute. Pray for us, will you, Lydia?"

"You know I will, Pierre."

The next morning the seigneur looked calm and at peace with himself. Lydia knew at once that he had won his mental battle and was now ready to accept for all time the will of God.

She attended High Mass with Pierre and his father in the new chapel, for this was to be the occasion of its blessing. That High Mass is said to have been the most magnificent ever celebrated in New France.

Watching Monsieur LeBer as he knelt in prayer,

Lydia realized how fortunate she was to have been placed in the custody of such an honorable man.

"I am grateful, O Lord, for my blessings," she prayed.

10.

Sister Sainte-Madeleine

"Lydia, I have news for you," said Monsieur LeBer one late September morning as the two came into the house after attending Mass in the new chapel.

"The governor of Massachusetts has demanded a list of all English captives now being held here in New France. The intendant took your name yesterday. It may mean that soon—next month, possibly —there will be an exchange of prisoners."

Lydia stared in amazement. So much had happened recently in the LeBer household that she had given little thought to her own future.

"Would it make you very happy," asked her guardian, "to return to Groton?" He smiled at her affectionately.

"Oh, no, sir," cried Lydia. She spoke with so much feeling that Monsieur LeBer was startled. "I don't want to go back. Must I? My family is all gone. Even John, for all I know, is still with the Indians. Where would I live? What would I do?" Tears of alarm filled her blue eyes.

Monsieur LeBer sighed in relief and leaned over to pat her arm. "We don't want you ever to leave here, my dear," he said kindly. "But I wasn't sure how you felt. In all fairness, I had to give you the opportunity to return to your own English people —to your relatives and friends. I'm sure I would have enough influence to see that you were included if such an exchange were arranged."

"I'd dread to return to Groton now, sir. How could I look upon the remains of my former home? Besides, I feel I have made a life for myself here with all of you. Perhaps I can find something to do to be of service, Monsieur. Do you think it likely?"

"Don't worry about that, my child," the seigneur assured her. "You are such a comfort right here in my home. I feel as if you were a second daughter to me. If time drags we can find something to occupy you. And don't fear that you will be forced to return if you don't want to. You are an adult and so have the right to make your own choice."

During the weeks that followed there was more news about the exchange of captives. In October twenty-two captives from Quebec were returned to the English in Boston. Forty-two others, including Lydia Longley and Mary Genevieve Sayward, remained in New France.

In March of 1696 Lydia made the most important decision of her life. For many months, she had felt herself drawn toward Catholicism. Still she was tormented by doubts. How could she, a Puritan, ever become a Catholic? How could she feel as if she belonged? But she could not forever resist the grace of God. For almost two years Lydia had lived with a devout family who had brought her nearer and nearer to the Church. She had learned to understand the Mass and the sacraments, the meaning of vicarious sacrifice, the value of prayers for the dead. Now every minute of daily morning Mass was precious to her. How she longed to be able to receive Holy Communion!

After Lydia had made her decision to stay in Ville-Marie, it seemed that one more barrier had been removed from her path. Early in March she walked over to Bonsecours Church. God's grace was surely at work. She knelt alone at the altar rail, her eyes on the miraculous statue of the Blessed Virgin.

"Dear Mother of God, help me to come to a decision. Tell me what to do."

Lydia closed her eyes and suddenly her doubts fled. The problem disappeared. Why was she waiting when she knew that only in Christ's Church would she find peace? Gratefully and determinedly she rose, genuflected, and left. As she closed the door, she was surprised to find herself facing Pierre. With moist eyes she told him, "I'm going to become a Catholic, Pierre. At last I know what I should do. I have no more doubts."

"I'm glad, Lydia." Pierre grasped her hand. "My prayers for you are being answered. How odd that today, of all days, I should come to this church, not knowing that you were here! Do you remember the first time we came here together? I lighted a candle."

"I remember." Lydia nodded.

"I asked God then to give you the gift of faith. Father will be so pleased——and my sister, too. This hope has been close to our hearts for a long time."

Lydia and Pierre walked down the aisle to kneel together in thanksgiving at the altar rail. As they left the church, Lydia said, "Did you notice, Pierre? The Blessed Virgin seemed to be smiling directly at us. This grace is surely the blessing which Mother Bourgeoys said I might receive from her."

There was much rejoicing when Lydia's friends heard of her wish to become a Catholic. Monsieur LeBer himself was delighted. "Dear Lydia, I am very happy for you," he declared with warmth. "We have prayed for this."

Madeleine de Maricourt smiled and told Lydia she had known all along that some day she would embrace the faith. "As I once told you, you have much to bring to the Church."

Monsieur Meriel's handclasp was warm as he expressed his happiness and spoke of the instructions she must have before her baptism.

When Lydia went to the convent to speak with

Mother Bourgeoys about her conversion, she was moved to tears.

"I am an old woman, my child," said the beloved foundress, drawing Lydia down beside her. "I am tired, and I have to stay in my room more and more. But there is something I should love to do, if you will let me. Will you stay here in the mother house so that I may instruct you? I would so like to do that. You have such a quick and intelligent mind, it would be a pleasure for me to add what knowledge I have of religious truths to the gift of faith which the Lord has already given to you."

For a moment Lydia could barely speak, so overwhelmed was she by this proof of Mother Bourgeoys' affection. "It would be a great honor, indeed, Mother, to have for my teacher the foundress of the Congregation. I thank you with all my heart." And so Lydia Longley, girl captive from Groton, lived for a month in the peace and serenity of the convent.

When Jeanne LeBer heard of Lydia's intention to embrace the faith, she asked if the baptism could take place in the convent chapel, for she wished to be an unseen guest at the christening of the girl who had become a member of her father's household.

Special permission was obtained from the bishop of Quebec.

On Tuesday, April 24, 1696, shortly after her twenty-second birthday, Lydia Longley was baptized. Her beloved benefactor, Monsieur Jacques LeBer, and her good friend, Madeleine de Maricourt, were her godparents as she received the name Lydia-Madeleine. Later, as Mother Bourgeoys and the other sisters gathered around to congratulate her, she couldn't help thinking of the beautiful silent witness behind the altar.

The next morning Lydia-Madeleine received Holy Communion for the first time, surrounded by loving friends in the Congregation chapel. She seemed filled with tranquility as she asked God's blessing on her family in heaven and on these dear ones now so close to her.

Lydia went back to Monsieur LeBer's, but she felt different somehow. The weeks she had spent in the serenity of the convent had made a deep and lasting impression on her. She had taken part in the spiritual exercises of the sisters and observed their devotion. She had admired their industry. Most of all she had loved the schoolrooms. She found herself recalling nostalgically the family lessons at home in Groton.

How she had loved teaching Richard, Joseph, and Jemima! She knew she would welcome association with youngsters once more.

As time passed, Lydia began to hope that perhaps her own future might lie there in the congregation as a teaching sister. Perhaps whatever talent she had might be dedicated to the service of God.

At first, thoughts of leaving Monsieur LeBer troubled her. He had lost his daughter and soon Pierre would be gone. But he was a busy man, occupied with his own work, and she reasoned that it wasn't as if she were going to enter a cloistered community. He could come often to see her.

For some months she waited, testing the sincerity of her vocation. Finally she approached Mother Bourgeoys and confided her secret hope.

"I believe, Lydia, that you would make a fine sister. To tell the truth, I have often hoped that in time you might turn to the convent. You will be the first girl from New England to enter. Life within is not easy, my child," the elderly sister cautioned, "but, knowing how much you have suffered already, I have no doubt that you can face rigorous discipline. I shall do all in my power to help you if you decide to join our community."

Before the final days of 1696, Lydia-Madeleine's application for entrance into the Congregation de Notre Dame as a novice was accepted, and she left the foster home where she had been treated with such affection. The name she received was Sister Sainte-Madeleine.

On June 25, 1698, the novice Sister Sainte-Madeleine was present in the Congregation chapel when twenty-four sisters took simple vows of poverty, chastity, and obedience, as well as a vow to teach. The day before, the Congregation de Notre Dame had become a permanent order, and the community had accepted and signed the rule approved by the bishop.

There were many distinguished people present at this ceremony, including Sister Sainte-Madeleine's good friend, Monsieur Meriel, Vicar-General Dollier de Casson, and the great Bishop Saint-Vallier. Sister Sainte-Madeleine knew that this was one of the happiest days of Mother Bourgeoys' life.

From her seat the novice watched with feeling the faces of the sisters as, one after another, they pronounced their final vows and received from the bishop their names in religion. Seated nearby was her dear friend, Mary Genevieve Sayward, who had entered the community that very year and was called Sister of the Angels.

On September 19, 1699, Sister Sainte-Madeleine took her final vows as a nun. She is mentioned in the records as a devout religious and one who gained the esteem of her entire community. Because of her unusual courage and prudence, she was later sent to the Isle of Orléans as superior of the Convent of the Holy Family.

After many years of religious life, Sister Sainte-Madeleine died in Montreal. On July 21, 1758, she was buried in the Chapel of the Infant Jesus in the parish church, the first woman of United States birth to become a religious.

Epilogue

Lydia Longley was one of the few English captives, if not the only one, taken into a French family as a ward. Most captives worked in service to their benefactors. Many of these English captives chose to remain in New France when given the opportunity to return to Puritan New England. Some married and others entered the religious life. A number stayed with the Indians, but it is said that only about one out of one hundred captives was barbarized to Indian civilization.

John Longley lived with the Abenaki Indians for four years and was so reluctant to leave that he had to be forced to return to his home. In Groton he married twice. Six children were born of his union with Sarah Prescott and six more from a later marriage with Deborah Houghton. Thus the name of Longley was preserved. John served as a deacon in the Groton church and held town office. He died in 1750 and is buried in the old Groton cemetery.

There is a tradition, but no proof, that Jemima Longley survived scalping at the hands of the Indians.

Jeanne LeBer died in the fifty-third year of her

life on October 3, 1714. In 1768 the buildings of
the Congregation de Notre Dame were destroyed
by fire, and no trace of Jeanne LeBer's cell was left.
A new church was afterward built on the founda-
tions of the old. A vestment which she embroidered
is still in existence.

In 1706, ten years after Lydia entered the congregation, Samuel Williams of Deerfield, Massachusetts, the sixteen-year-old son of the Reverend
John Williams, also a captive, lived in Monsieur
LeBer's home. On December 21, 1707, he was baptized a Catholic by Monsieur Meriel.

Pierre LeBer and François Charron did found a
community of Frères Hospitallers, Hospital Brothers, which never reached full development. Because
Pierre had a special devotion to Saint Anne, he built
the first church dedicated to her in Montreal. The
first Mass was celebrated there in 1698. He loved
to paint, and in 1700 he did a portrait of Mother
Bourgeoys from memory. He died in 1707 at the
age of thirty-eight.

Monsieur Meriel kept remarkable records of the
English captives in early Canada. He lived a life of
self-sacrifice and hard work at the Hotel-Dieu as
chaplain to those nursing sisters and as director of

the pupils and sisters of the Congregation de Notre Dame. His knowledge of English enables us, to this day, to identify those captives of the seventeenth century. He died on January 12, 1713, at the age of fifty-two.

About a mile from the center of the beautiful town of Groton, Massachusetts, is a monument by the side of a country road. It was placed by the Groton Historical Society near the site of the house once occupied by the Longley family. It reads:

"Near this spot dwelt William and Deliverance
Longley with their eight children.
On the 27th of July, 1694, the Indians killed the
father and mother and five of the children, and
carried into captivity the other three."

Acknowledgments

For assisting me in collecting the material for this book, for helping me in translations, and for valuable criticism and suggestions, I express my appreciation to the following:

Mrs. Robert May, Curator of the Boutwell House, Groton, Massachusetts

Mrs. Howard Longley, Librarian, Shirley, Massachusetts

Mr. and Mrs. Forrest Wing, Shirley, Massachusetts

Mother Eugenie, Principal, Country Day School of the Holy Union, Groton, Massachusetts

Mrs. Roger Moore, Groton, Massachusetts

Miss Clarissa Coburn, Librarian, Groton, Massachusetts

Mrs. Ruth Sheedy, Librarian, Groton, Massachusetts

Rev. Charles B. Ames, Groton, Massachusetts

Jules Bazin, Head Librarian, Municipal Library, Montreal, Canada

Sister Albina-Marie, Librarian, Rivier College, Nashua, New Hampshire

Miss Christine Rockwood, Librarian, Nashua, New Hampshire

Rev. Emile Dupont, Groton, Massachusetts

Sister Sainte-Marie-de-Pontmain, Congregation de
   Notre Dame, Montreal, Canada

Harpell's Press Cooperative, Gardenvale, Canada

Clifford Shipton, American Antiquarian Society,
   Worcester, Massachusetts

Mrs. John C. Beale, Groton, Massachusetts

Mr. and Mrs. Arthur R. Wilson, Groton, Massachusetts

VISION BOOKS